Genesis, Zen and Quantum Physics

A Fresh Look at the Theology and Science of Creation

~~~~~~~~~~~~~~~~~~~~~~~~~~~~~~~~~~

By Jeff A. Benner and Michael Calpino

"Genesis, Zen and Quantum Physics," by Jeff A. Benner and Michael Calpino. ISBN 978-1-60264-871-5.

Published 2011 by Virtualbookworm.com Publishing Inc., P.O. Box 9949, College Station, TX 77845, US. ©2011, Jeff A. Benner and Michael Calpino. All rights reserved. Any part of this book may be copied for educational purposes only, without prior permission.

Manufactured in the United States of America.

Table of Contents

The Quantum Translation of Genesis 1 - 3

Genesis 1

1 Within the Beginning, he filled the powers, the skies and the land. **2** The land, she existed empty and unfilled. And a chaos was over the faces of the deep. And the wind of the Powers brooded over the faces of the waters. **3** And he said, "the Powers be revealed by the light, and the light illuminated." **4** The Powers saw the beauty of the light and he divided the Powers between the ordered light and the chaotic darkness. **5** And he called the Powers for order "light" and for chaos he called "darkness." And there were Powers for watching chaos and Powers for illuminating order, a unified work in chaos.

6 And he said the Powers will spread out a sheet through waters. And he caused a separating out of the waters to waters. **7** And the Powers spread out the sheet separating out the waters from the bottom side belonging to the sheet and separating the water out from the top side belonging to the sheet. And he stood firm. **8** And he called the Powers belonging to the sheet "sky." And there were Powers for watching chaos and Powers for illuminating order, a second work in chaos.

9 And he said, "The Powers will gather and watch the waters from under the skies move toward one place and dry land will be presented." And he stood firm. **10** And he called the Powers belonging to the dry ground "land," and he called the waters belonging to the collection, "sea." And the Powers saw the beauty. **11** And he said, "Powers bring forth young green plants on the land. Sow seed of fruit trees, producing fruit for its

continuing its offspring whose seed is in it all over the land."
And he stood firm. **12** The Land brought forth young green
plants, sowing seed, for continuing his offspring. And trees
produced fruit whose seed is in it for continuing its offspring.
And the Powers saw the beauty. **13** And there were Powers for
watching chaos and Powers for illuminating order, a third work
in chaos.

14 And he said, "Powers become a great light in the sheet of the
skies for a dividing between the light and the darkness. And
they are placed there for marking the way and for a witness and
for working chaos and for years." **15** And they were set as lights
in the sheet of the skies for the lighting over the land and he
stood firm. **16** And he made the powers, the two large lights and
the stars, the large light for a ruler of the work in chaos and the
small light for a ruler of the darkness. **17** And he gave them
Powers in the sheet of the skies for the light over the land.
18 And for ruling within a work in chaos and within the
darkness and for separating between the light and the chaotic
darkness, and the Powers saw the beauty. **19** And there were
Powers for watching chaos and Powers for illuminating order, a
fourth work in chaos.

20 And he said, "The Powers swarm the waters, a swarm of
nefesh chayah. And a flyer flies over the land, over the faces of
the sheet of the skies. **21** And the Powers filled the big tananim
and all nefesh of the chayah the crawling one who swarms the
waters to her bloodline and all flyers of the wing to her
bloodline. And the Powers saw the beauty. **22** And the Powers
knelt to them to say bear fruit and become great and complete,
the waters in the seas and the flyers will become great in the

land. **23** And there were Powers for watching chaos and Powers for illuminating order, a fifth work in chaos.

24 And he said, "Powers bring forth the nefesh chayah of the land to her bloodline, a walker and a crawler and his chayah of land belonging to her bloodline." And he stood firm. **25** And the Powers aligned the chayah of the land to her bloodline and the walker to her bloodline and all the crawler of the ground to his bloodline. And the Powers saw the beauty. **26** And the Powers said, "We will make an adam in our shadow, like our origin. And they journeyed among the swimmers of the sea and among the flyers of the skies and among the walkers and among all the land and among all the crawlers over the land." **27** And he commanded and the Powers filled the man with his shadow, with the shadow of the Powers he filled him, mind and womb he filled them. **28** The Powers knelt to them and the Powers said to them, "Bear fruit and become great, and complete the land and rule her, and journey among the swimmers of the sea and among the fliers of the skies and among all the chayah crawling on the land." **29** And the Powers said, "Look, I gave to you(plural) the whole green plant, a seeding of seed which is over the face of all the land and the whole of the tree which in him a fruit tree a seeding a seed, for you(plural). He will mediate for food." **30** "And all green plants are for all the life of the land and for all the flyers of the skies and for all the crawlers over the land which is in him nefesh chayah." And he stood firm. **31** And the Powers saw all that he became and look, an all encompassing beauty. And there were Powers for watching chaos and Powers for illuminating order, the sixth work in chaos.

Genesis 2

1 And they were completed, the sky and the land and all their army. **2** And he completed the Powers in the seventh work of chaos, his instructions which he filled and he stopped in the seventh work of chaos, from all his instructions which he filled. **3** And the Powers knelt on the seventh work in chaos and He(Powers) assigned him(Shabbat) because in him He(Ayn Soph) stopped from all his instructions which he filled the Powers for function.

4 These are offspring of the skies and land in their being made full, in a work of chaos YHVH the Powers made land and skies. **5** And all plant life of the field, that existed before in the land and all plants of the field before they will grow because YHVH the Powers had not caused rain over the land and without an adam for serving the ground. **6** And mist came up from the land and gave drink to all the faces of the ground. **7** And YHVH the Powers pressed out the adam of the multitude from Ha'adamah. And he blew into his nostrils a nesh'mat chayim and the adam existed for the nefesh chayah.

8 And YHVH the Powers established a protected region in Eden from ancient times. And he placed there the adam whom he molded. **9** And YHVH the Powers grew from the ground all the trees that were pleasing to the sight and good for food, trees of the chayim in the middle of the protected region and the trees of the experience of function and dysfunction. **10** And a river comes out from eden to give drink to the protected region and from there it spreads out. And it goes to the four kings. **11** The name of the one is Pishon. It is the one that circles around all the land of the Havilah, where the gold is. **12** And the gold of that land is beautiful. The b'dolach is there and the shoham stone. **13** And the name of the second river is Gihon. It is the one that circles around the land of Cush. **14** And the name of the third river is Hiddekel. It is the one that walks the ancient path. And the fourth river, it is the Parat.

15 And YHVH the Powers took the adam and he settled him in the protected region of Eden to work her and to protect her. **16** And YHVH the Powers commanded over the man saying, "from all the trees of the protected region you will utterly devour." **17** "And from the trees of the experience of function and dysfunction you will not eat from them because in the day you eat from them, a death you will die."

18 And YHVH the Powers said, "It is not good for the existence of the adam to be alone, I will provide for him a helper like his story." **19** And YHVH the Powers pressed out from Ha'adamah all the chayah of the field and all the flyers of the skies. And He(YHVH) came to the adam to see who he would call to himself, and all that he will call to himself, the adam of nefesh, that will become his character/breath. **20** And the adam met the characters/breaths belonging to all the walkers, and to the flyers of the skies and to all the chayah of the field. And for adam no helper was found like his story.

21 And YHVH the Powers fell as a trance on the adam and he slept. And he took a unity from his tzel'ot and he closed flesh under it. **22** And YHVH the Powers rebuilt the tzela that he took from the adam for a woman and she came to the adam. **23** And the adam spoke this poem, "bone from my bone and flesh from my flesh." Because of this he will meet woman because from the man she had received this. **24** Therefore man will leave his father and his mother and he will join in his woman and they will become unified flesh. **25** And the two of them were enlightened beings, the adam and his woman, and they were not disappointed in each other.

Genesis 3

1 And the nechash had been enlightened from out of all the chayah of the field who YHVH the Powers made. And he said to the woman of passion, "Because the Powers said 'you(plural) will not eat from all the trees of the protected place.'" **2** But the woman said to the nachash, "From the fruit of the trees of the protected region we will eat." **3** "And from the fruit of the trees that are in the middle of the protected region the Powers said 'you(plural) will not eat from them and you(plural) will not approach them or you will die.'" **4** And the nechash said to the woman, "No, 'a death will you die.'" **5** "For the Powers know for in the day of your(plural) eating from them and your(plural) eyes will be opened and you(plural) will be like the Powers knowing function and dysfunction."

6 And the woman saw that the function of the tree was for food and that it was a delight to the eyes and the tree was desirable for knowledge. And she took from its fruit and she ate and she gave also to her man with her and he ate. **7** And the eyes of the two of them opened and they knew that they were enlightened and they sewed fig leaves and they made themselves aprons.

8 And they heard the sound of YHVH the Powers walking in the protected region because of the wind of the work in chaos. And the adam and his woman hid themselves from the face of YHVH the Powers in the middle of the trees of the protected region. **9** And YHVH the Powers called to the Adam and said to him, "How?" **10** And he said, "Your sound I heard in the protected region and I was afraid because I am enlightened and I hid myself." **11** And he said, "Who proclaimed to you that you were enlightened? The tree species which I commanded you to not eat from, you ate." **12** And the adam said, "The woman who you gave my support, she gave to me from the trees and I ate." **13** And YHVH the Powers said to the woman, "What is this you did?" And the woman said, "The nechash deceived me and I ate." **14** And YHVH the Powers said to the nechash, "Because you did this, cursed are you from all the walkers and from all the chayah of the field. On your belly she will walk and the multitude you will eat all the days of your life." **15** "And enmity I will make between you and the woman, and between your seed and her seed. He will strike you, the head, and you will strike us, the heel." **16** To the woman he says, "I will greatly increase the your labor and your pregnancy, in pain you will bear children and to your man is your desire and he will rule in you." **17** And to Adam he said, "Because you listened to the voice of your woman and you ate from the tree which I commanded you saying, 'you will not eat from him,' the ground is cursed in your production. In pain you will eat of her all the days of your life." **18** "And she(the ground) will cause brambles and weeds to grow for you and you will eat the green plants of the field." **19** "With the sweat of your nostrils you will eat bread again. You returned to Ha'adamah given that from her you were taken, given that a multitude are you and to the multitude you will return."

20 And Adam met the character of his woman. He declared that she was the mother of all the living ones. **21** YHVH of the Powers made for the adam and his woman coverings of skin and he clothed them. **22** And YHVH the Powers said, "Look the man is like a unity apart from us knowing function and dysfunction and now turning, will send his hand and will take also from the trees of the chayim and will eat and live forever." **23** And YHVH of the Powers sent him from the protected region in Eden to serve Ha'adamah, which is where he was taken from. **24** And he cast out the adam. And he caused the keruvim and the lahat of the revolving sword, to dwell from the ancient times for the protected region in Eden, to guard the road of the trees of life.

Introduction to the Quantum Translation and Commentary

The translation you have just read is the product of years of work in a very unique environment. Obviously, the language is very different from most translations you may be familiar with. The authors decided early on in the project to emphasize accuracy of translation over ease of reading because of the belief that by accurately translating the meaning of the words, less of the author's own theology and philosophy would be inserted.

There were several considerations taken into account as the translation developed. As previously mentioned, accuracy of definition was one. The second was to consider how the words were understood in the time they were written and even when the oral traditions on which that account was based was developed. The authors attempted to put themselves in the place of the desert nomad, not only physically but mentally. Before the Greeks made abstract thought popular millennia later, the people who transmitted these stories had a completely different value system and way of looking at the world. We do a disservice by imposing our worldview on their account.

A crucial component of the translation is the use of the ancient Hebrew pictographs. This was especially helpful in understanding words whose meanings may have changed over the centuries or whose use in the text no longer made sense.

As the project continued, it became obvious to the authors that the implications of the translation were profound. Much of what Christianity, and to a degree Judaism, has accepted as true could not be supported from the text. The story of creation provides the foundation for our understanding of God, ourselves, the universe and our relation to, and place within, it. If we use the text to support our philosophy and theology rather than letting our theology and philosophy arise from the text, our foundation will be built on sand rather than rock. If we have a flawed concept of whom and what God is, who we are and what our role in the world is, we will never reach our potential and will, in fact, make our lives and the world dysfunctional. The history of western religious tradition provides ample evidence that its theology and the practical implications thereof are far afield of the truth.

Another implication discovered by the authors that supported a hypothesis they held going into the study was that science and the creation account were not adversaries but close friends. In fact, while the language of modern physics may have been unknown to the ancients, its concepts are complementary to a proper reading of the account. In fact, the Genesis story's understanding of the physical universe may rival our own.

Finally, the authors remained open to interpretations of the text that may have developed outside the Judeo-Christian tradition. This, of course, may be heretical to some but people all over the world have searched for the meaning of life and God and if we are all created the same way, there is no reason to assume implicitly that one religious tradition has more value than another. In fact, while the outward expressions of the religious traditions of the world may be very different, the mystical subsets of each bear striking similarities in both theology and practice. Meditation and prayer have similar forms whether they are derived from the Kabbalah of Judaism, the monasteries of Christianity or the temples of Buddhism. The truly striking thing is that these "mystical" practices gave rise to similarities in theology that are difficult to explain given the divergent history and geography of the traditions from which they have arisen. The authors have come to the conclusion that within each of these traditions there are those who have sought and found a connection with the divine and irregardless of the forms and rituals of religion, there is singular "method" of making that connection. It is the journey that results in that connection that will reveal the truth about the world, God and ourselves.

Now, a word about the environment that produced this translation and commentary. The authors are eternally indebted to all the people who made up the religious community we called Beit HaKadosh in Reading, Pennsylvania. Beit HaKadosh was based on a singular idea. If we recreated the community of the Bible, if we discovered what it was they knew or what lifestyle characteristics they had, if we could uncover their theology and practice untainted by millennia of "heresy," we would have their results. As all such things are, it was a learning process and every person, whether they stayed for days, months or years, contributed in some way to that process.

We began with the realization that the outward practice of Christianity, its holidays and traditions, are not rooted in Scripture. There was no question in our minds that the practice of Judaism permeated both the "Old" and "New" Testaments and it was there we needed to begin. As we learned, it was not just the practice, but the theology of the Judeo-Christian tradition that made little sense scripturally or logically. As we looked back beyond the appearance of Y'shua (Jesus) and the conquest of the Greeks to David and Moshe (Moses) and Avraham, we encountered a cultural divide that would have to be crossed. It was not the simple differences we see between the French and English but a completely different worldview and way of thinking. The culture of the Greeks, from whom we get our worldview, and the Ancient Hebrews, are completely different, and in

11

many ways, opposite. It was also the differences between the nomadic society of Avraham and the settled life of the city state from which we are descended that added to the gulf of misunderstanding.

We realized there were two things that we needed to change, our thinking and our lifestyle. Fortunately, we had developed a unique community at Beit HaKadosh. After the more "formal" service and teaching, we would have a "potluck" lunch and sit around for hours talking about various topics. What was truly unusual was the freedom we allowed ourselves. No topic was off limits, no question unworthy of being explored. We had people from a variety of backgrounds with wide bases of Biblical and historical knowledge who would contribute to the discussion. The crucial component of the discussion was that during the process, no solution was rejected or accepted until good reason, history and Scriptural consistency could back it up. No one was accepted as having a lock on the truth and anyone and anything could be questioned. While they were serious discussions, no one was judgmental and humor lightened things up. We were in a pursuit of truth but we maintained a relaxed and accepting atmosphere where "heretical" ideas were evaluated honestly and it was only those who thought they had all the answers and sat in judgment of others that were in danger of "excommunication."

While we developed some unique answers to questions everyone and no one asks, it was clear that intellectual exercise alone was insufficient. It didn't take us long to realize the western worldview, with its values and assumptions, was counterintuitive. A consumer culture based on knowledge is the polar opposite of the experiential and nomadic culture of the great men and women, not just of the Bible, but of most religious traditions. We came to the rather startling conclusion, at least to our western minds, that it is our lifestyle that produces our theology and not our theology that produces our lifestyle. In the Christian tradition in particular, one goes through a "conversion," a change of mind if you will, about the facts of God and the universe. This change in thinking is supposed to produce a change in lifestyle; it is expected to create in the converted a new set of values and practices. The problem is, the set of values and practices found in the Bible is in direct opposition to the prevailing culture and the pressure to conform to that culture is too strong. In short, that is why Rome changed Christianity and Christianity didn't change Rome. It was obvious that through an honest evaluation of the biographies of the Bible, only one conclusion could be reached. From Avraham to Moshe to David to Elisha to Peter, James and John, the men and women of the Bible who "saw God" either adopted a nomadic lifestyle or were brought up in it. It was clear that the values and worldview developed in an individual who lives such a lifestyle is an essential ingredient in revelation. It was this realization and the attempt by some of us to adopt it in a practical fashion that led to the dissolution of Beit HaKadosh.

The purpose of the preceding paragraphs is to give the reader an understanding of the journey the authors have undertaken that led to the development of the written work before you. Unfortunately, what you have is only a snapshot in time, a static account of the dynamic process that is our growth in "wisdom and stature." The authors, as men who continue to add to incomplete knowledge and experience glimpses of revelation, will continue the journey far beyond what you hold in your hands. It is our hope that by opening your mind and spirit, you will be challenged and rewarded on your own journey by honestly and thoughtfully evaluating what we have found on ours.

Commentary on the Quantum Translation

The following is a detailed commentary on our translation where we dig deep into the language and culture of the ancient Hebrews, the authors of this text. One thing that must always be kept in mind as you read this, is that the ancient cultures of the Near East perceive the world around them very differently than we do in our modern Greco-Roman culture. If we attempt to interpret this ancient text from a modern perspective, we will undoubtedly misinterpret and mistranslate that text.

Genesis 1:1

בְּרֵאשִׁית בָּרָא אֱלֹהִים אֵת הַשָּׁמַיִם וְאֵת הָאָרֶץ:

Within the Beginning, he filled the powers, the skies and the land.

We begin at the beginning and in so doing; we shall take a look at all the components of the words in the sentence and explain their significance. The letter ב (beit) before the word רֵאשִׁית (reshit) means within, in, or inside. Our translation loosely follows the understanding presented in the *Zohar*[1]. "By means of a beginning (it) created *Elohim* (the powers)"[2]. In our translation, however, the 'Beginning' is an 'entity' itself, which is why it is capitalized. "The Beginning" is that which existed before creation and has always existed. It is indefinable, it is beyond our understanding, it is the totality of all creation from which everything we see and know came forth. In the Kabbalah this 'thing' is called *Ayn Soph* which, loosely translated, means 'without borders' or 'without definition.' The *Zohar* continues, "The most mysterious power enshrouded in the limitless clave, as it were, without cleaving its void, remaining wholly unknowable until from the force of the strokes there shone forth a supernal and mysterious point. Beyond that there is no knowable, and therefore is called Reshit, the creative utterance which is the starting point of all." Such language could easily be construed as a description of the Big Bang. In Isaiah 41:4 'God' is called the Beginning although, by labeling it 'God,' we may cause confusion. Some of the attributes we normally ascribe God such as, all-present, all powerful and the like, *Ayn Soph* is but, we also use words like 'father,' 'king,' 'the man on the

---

[1] A collection of Kabbalistic teachings.
[2] *Zohar* Bereshith 1:1

16

throne,' to describe God. To put *Ayn Soph* in such relational terms is to go contrary to his only definition which is 'without definition.' *Ayn Soph* is not a name, a person or a thing to be described. It is *beyond* person so we can use 'it' when referring to it. It is no-thing although this no-thing is not the opposite of *some*thing. It is like the emptiness of space yet we know that space is not devoid of matter. It is energy that has no mass yet it gives substance to all things. It is within this power, this force, this *thing* that is completely beyond our ability to describe, that creation, as we know it, took shape. Because of this similarity in concept, we will refer to this creative force as *Ayn Soph*.

Ayn Soph is infinite yet we know that creation is finite in the form in which we experience it. It can be described, experienced. Yet it is *Ayn Soph* as well for there is nothing apart from it. All of the created order is made of the 'stuff of God.' Everything within *Ayn Soph* that we know as the created order, on all its various levels of reality, only one of which is physical, is *Elohim* which we have translated as 'the powers.' (*Elohim* is the plural form of *elo'ah* - power). The ancient Hebrew pictographs for the word *El*, the root of *Elohim* are an ox head (𐤀) and a staff or yoke (𐤋) - the ox in the yoke representing the "mighty power that does work."

This idea that everything is made of the stuff of God, that all is intertwined within the whole of *Ayn Soph*, can be a great blessing. In the five centuries since the Enlightenment, man has gone from being the center of the universe to being an insignificant biological accident in a vast universe that could care less about him. There are two reactions to this idea. There are those that reject modern science and understanding and cling to an un-provable and irrational belief in a personal God regardless of their experience. As long as they don't look too closely with their mind and remain in an emotionally invested attitude, they believe there is something 'out there' that cares about

17

them personally. They pray, they hope, they believe- even in the face of clear evidence to the contrary. Their prayers are often not answered yet they rationalize "It was God's will that this child got cancer and died a horrible death" or any of a million other tragic or misfortunate occurrences. The belief that there is a God like us-personal, emotional, willing yet unable or able and not willing to bless us-is a throwback to the pagan belief that if we do this ritual, say these prayers or offer this sacrifice, that there is a power over us that will, *hopefully*, listen and act on our behalf. For those who have prayed for a sick child or to relieve some other horrible suffering and seen nothing, such an entity is either cruel or impotent.

On the other hand, if we believe we are merely the result of a series of biological accidents then we have a different problem. Man thinks and behaves individually and in society and our behavior has rules, for lack of a better term. Also, because we think, because we are 'self aware,' we seek the meaning of our existence. If we are merely accidents, simple chemical functions that follow the rules of science with no inherent value or direction, the search for meaning or the foundation for the rules of a 'good' society are pointless. There are no ultimate answers; there is no foundation for morality. The world is governed simply by survival of the fittest and there are no consequences for our behavior other than what is immediate. Anything goes, the strongest wins. All the things we value-fairness, freedom, justice, morality-only have value because we have decided they have value. If we decide otherwise, that's okay because the new morals and ideals will have no more intrinsic value than did the old. Western democracies and brutal tyrannies are morally equal. Mother Theresa and Ted Bundy are morally equivalent. They just chose a different morality. I don't think any of us want to live in such a world.

So what is left? The Chumash[3] makes an interesting observation here. It gives this possible translation. "The world was created for the sake of the things that are called 'beginning.'" This idea places purpose back into creation. Not only that, but it gives intrinsic value to everything in it. As we stated earlier, everything is made of the 'stuff of God,' everything has a small part of the infinite within it. That being true, you and I become the center of the universe. That may sound egotistical but if the universe is infinite, every spot within it is the center. If all is made of the infinite, we are all share equally in that infinite quality and substance and we each have the value that reality entails. Everything in the world, including people, has value because of what they are and not because of what they can do. We have intrinsic value, not utilitarian value. And because of the intrinsic value of all things, because it is all made of the stuff of God, everything has purpose and direction, the universe unfolds in an orderly way. It is not a series of accidents but the result of intelligence. Not the intelligence of personality and will, but of law and purpose. We will define this intelligence, purpose and the values it creates in later verses.

One final point before we leave this subject. This idea of the unity of all things is not just philosophy or metaphysics; it is a crucial part of Quantum theory. Henry Stapp said that the physical world is "not a structure built out of independently existing unanalyizable entities, but rather a web of relationships between elements whose meanings arise wholly from their relationships to the whole."[4] This unity of all things is demonstrated at the sub atomic level and this interconnectedness defines and gives meaning to everything within the whole. Everything relates to and affects everything else. This idea

---

[3] The Torah, the first five books of Moses.

[4] Henry Stapp, "S Matrix Interpretation of Quantum Theory," Lawrence Berkeley Laboratory preprint, June 22, 1970

is related to the 'Butterfly Effect,' the idea that the flapping of the wings of a butterfly in China can give birth to a hurricane in the Caribbean. That's a demonstration of how things connect on a natural level but we know our own lives are changed every moment by choices made not only by ourselves but by the billions of others on the planet. Every action, every word, has an effect on the unfolding of the history of the planet and we may never know ninety-nine percent of those consequences. We know the good stories, like a teacher who gave a word of encouragement at the right time and turned a student around who later made a big impact. But what about the actions that shaped monsters like Hitler or Bundy. Billions of moments, each shaped by millions of people all interconnected to lead us to where we are now. All things interconnected within the whole of *Ayn Soph*. Not random at all but intelligent and purposeful. Again, we will define those things as we move along, for now, back to our translation.

Because this verse is a summary verse covering all of creation, we cannot separate the *Elohim*, the sky and the land. Since all of the created order is *Elohim*, including the sky and the land, all are a small part of the infinity that is *Ayn Soph*. We have chosen to use the simple sky and land rather than the usual 'heavens and earth' because the ancient peoples were more simplistic and concrete in their understanding of the universe and by using simple terms we are trying to recapture that flavor.

For those that know some of the Kabalistic view of God and the universe, the head of the Seferotic Tree is represented here. The *Elohim* corresponds to the Son, the Sky to *Abba* (Father) and the Earth to Ima (Mother). *Elohim* (or Y'shua), the son, being the first to emanate from *Ayn Soph*, or in the language of the New Testament, 'the firstborn of creation,' is the original force of separation of all that is the creation. The first three days of the creation story are the separation of the *Elohim* (light/darkness), the skies (water from water and sky) and the land (water and land). The second three days are the filling up of these things. The rest of the story will explain how all these things are 'filled up.' The word *bara* is usually translated as 'create' but is better translated as 'fattened' or 'filled up.' Notice an important ramification of this translation. The powers, the sky and the land are not created '*ex nihilo*' as is commonly understood. The *Elohim*, the sky and the land already exist and the creation story speaks of their separating and 'filling' or 'fattening.' This agrees with one of the fundamental ideas given us by Albert Einstein. Matter can neither be created or destroyed and according to that basic equation $E=MC^2$ matter and energy are interrelated and interchangeable. Energy becomes matter and matter becomes energy. This matter/energy that forms all the things of the universe is the 'stuff of God' we have been referring to. It is eternal and in our verse and present epoch it is combined in a way that makes the world recognizable to us. In other ages past they may have been combined differently and, even now, new combinations create different things. While eastern philosophy has understood this interrelationship of all things, it is not something integral to the western worldview.

Another crucial element in Biblical understanding that is lost in our western worldview is our view of time. In the western worldview time is linear. There was a beginning and there will be an end. The beginning is described in Gen 1:1 and before that there was nothing. Time marches forward to the conclusion of history. The eastern worldview of time, and the Biblical one I might add, is circular. History does not have a beginning and end, the world is not described as having a beginning and end. To those of you turned off by this notion as Hindu or Buddhist, keep in mind that before the time of Alexander's conquests, Judaism was an eastern and not a western religion and adhered to an Eastern/Semitic worldview. Moshe has much more in common with Hindu and Chinese philosophy and worldview than that of Plato and Aristotle's western world.

For the individual who believes in the Bible and respects a scientific understanding of the world, this way of looking at time brings harmony, which is usually the result of moving away from a dualistic western mindset. For example, the age of the dinosaurs and the ice age all could have happened during previous 'cycles' of time. This eliminates the conundrum that fundamentalists get themselves into. To a fundamentalist, western oriented bible scholar, the earth cannot be very old. They find themselves arguing with the current scientific paradigm which says the world is billions of years old. But both the Christian and the scientist are arguing from the same western worldview where time is concerned. Both, however, need to ignore some of the evidence in order to make their idea of the origins of the universe and the world work. The Biblical scholar needs to ignore the scientific support for an uniformitarian view of the world, a view that says the forces that shape the world today are basically the same as they were in the past. This leads to the formation of sedimentary rock or the erosion of mountains that make the Appalachians different from the Rockies. The scientist however, needs to ignore evidence like the presence of humans and dinosaurs together in the fossil record, that cataclysms have had a part in shaping the world, and the preposterous notion that random mutation is solely responsible for the creation of the great variety of life on the planet.

The Bible itself presents a circular view of time. 'There is nothing new under the sun...' The circular nature of time is obvious in the march of the seasons and years, the sabbatical and jubilee cycles. The Book of Judges presents a microcosm of the circular view of the history of man, both in an individual and a corporate sense. A circle of repentance, righteousness, backsliding, wickedness and judgment, leading to repentance. Now let us look at the larger picture. The Bible presents at least four cycles of creation and destruction. The first is from Genesis One to the fall of man, the second is from Genesis three to Noah, the third from Noah to the return of Messiah and the fourth from His return to the *re*creation of the 'heavens and the earth.' Who can say that there were not an infinite number of these cycles before Genesis and who can say there will not be more after the close of Revelation? As stated previously, Genesis 1:1 does not speak of the 'creating' of the sky and the land, but their being filled up. Also, the new sky and land the prophets speak of are the renewing[5] of the sky and land. We also know that according to the cycles described in the Bible, there are things and people that survive from one cycle to the next. It could very well be that the salvation described in the Bible is the ability to move on to the next cycle just as Noah did and those who live through the wrath of God will. The largest cycle is universal, referred to as the 'oscillation' theory where the universe begins with the big bang (cataclysmic creation), expansion and contraction (history in the cycle) and implosion/big bang (cataclysm/creation). Within this universal cycle is the solar cycle in which stars and planets live and die. Within the solar cycle are planetary cycles including those of our planet where things are created and destroyed over thousands of years down to the yearly cycle of seedtime and harvest and the daily cycle of night and day.

---

[5] The Hebrew word for "new" may mean new, renew, refresh or rebuild.

Genesis 1:2

וְהָאָרֶץ הָיְתָה תֹהוּ וָבֹהוּ וְחשֶׁךְ עַל־פְּנֵי תְהוֹם וְרוּחַ
אֱלֹהִים מְרַחֶפֶת עַל־פְּנֵי הַמָּיִם:

**The land, she existed empty and unfilled. And a chaos was
over the faces of the deep. And the wind of the Powers
brooded over the faces of the waters.**

One of the problems with the translation of Hebrew is that often the definitions are...indefinite. It is our intention to try to be as true to the *ancient* meaning and understanding of the words as possible, utilizing the ancient pictographs as well as the historical and cultural setting. In addition, we will attempt to give the words 'concrete' meaning whenever possible since the Hebrews thought in concrete terms rather than in the abstract. The verb *hayah* presents our first real challenge in this area. It is translated a multitude of ways throughout the Bible. Its meaning has to do with the essence of being and existence, something that has life that breathes. In this case, we translated it 'existed'[6]. In other words, the earth has 'being,' an idea reinforced by the use of the proper translation of the pronouns. In this case the earth, 'she,' was empty and unfilled. It is almost a sad situation and makes us look forward to the correction of the earth's sorry state, the healing of her 'depression.'

Water and chaos will be paralleled many times in this translation, in keeping with the poetic style of the passage, something often lost in the western translations. In this verse it is also analogous to 'the

---

[6] A few Hebrew verbs are used in a very generic sense such as with the verb *hayah*, literally meaning "to exist" but can be used in a wide range of applications.

deep.' To the ancient Hebrews, water, or specifically, the sea, was considered chaotic and unknown. We have translated the more common 'darkness' as chaos because it more accurately describes the situation before creation. The powers and all of the raw materials for the world as we know it were all jumbled together in chaos. It was as if there were light atoms and dark atoms all mixed together and the *Elohim* (powers) were both. I Kings 8:12 says that *Elohim* lives in a dark cloud and Isaiah 45:7 tells us that God created the darkness and the light, good and evil. *Elohim,* 'God,' is associated with both order/light/*shalom*[7] and chaos/darkness/evil. We often don't like to think of God as being involved with things we consider negative but there is nothing that is outside of God, or outside of *Ayn Soph*. Without the evil, we would not know the good. Without chaos we would not know order. Without darkness we couldn't appreciate the light. In Chinese culture this is the yin/yang, two opposing forces inextricably linked in the world.

There is a branch of physics devoted to the study of chaos, perhaps you have heard of 'chaos theory.' There have been some very interesting discoveries made within this arena. One of the most profound for the sake of our discussion is the discovery that the disorderly behavior of simple systems actually acted as a creative process. We postulated above that light and dark were 'jumbled up' in a chaotic state and that from this state order developed. Chaos theory has found that disorderly behavior generated complex, richly organized patterns, some of which were stable and some not, some that were finite and some that were not. Regardless of the outcome, they always developed with the "fascination of living things."[8] This

---

[7] A Hebrew word usually translated as 'peace' but, literally meaning whole and complete.

[8] *Chaos, Making a New Science* James Gleick, Viking Penguin Inc., New York 1987, p. 43

discovery is beginning to flush out what we described earlier as the 'intelligence' and purpose behind creation. The Second Law of Thermodynamics says that complex systems will degenerate over time into their simplest components and even Newton's Law of Motion requires the constant application of energy to overcome the forces that would stop motion and development. But within quantum theory we have something very different. For a Creation Scientist, it is God who provides the outside force that overcomes Newton's Law and the Second Law of Thermodynamics to create complexity. Quantum Theory states that the creative force exists within chaos itself. The chaos does not have to be acted upon. As an integral part of *Ayn Soph* it has the ability to act upon itself, to develop into more complex systems.

Let's take a closer look at this idea of chaos/darkness from a Hebraic perspective. The darkness is not, in this case, simply the absence of light. This darkness has substance; it can be felt as was the darkness that came upon Egypt during the plagues[9]. The *Torah*[10] says it could be felt, and not only that, it immobilized them. It is something piercing, painful, like the groping of a blind man. It was as if Moshe reached back through time and brought some of this completely 'unrefined' chaos into the strict order that was Egypt. At this point in our story nothing is 'living' or conscious. In Egypt, this chaos would have come into direct contact with the very ordered systems that are living things. This would have been very painful, no doubt.

The darkness is unutilized, potential energy as opposed to the light which is pure energy, substance being used. This true darkness can be felt as 'heaviness' which is the 'glory' of God. *Kavod*, a Hebrew word

---

[9] Exodus 10:21

[10] A Hebrew word meaning teaching, often translated as law, referring to the laws of the first five books of Moshe.

usually translated as 'glory,' literally means 'something heavy.' To experience the heaviness of God is to see him in his original, 'unrefined' and potential state, the moment before being, before things were separated out. No wonder Moshe could not experience God's 'glory' in its fullness, it was his heaviness. He would have been enveloped by it and returned to a state before his own being! But he did experience some of it. In order for that to happen we need to be stripped of the superfluous order we create for ourselves, our mental constructs of who we are, the 'I,' the ego, the things that only have reality in our own thoughts. Only stripped of our ego to our basic 'unrefined' state can we experience the 'unrefined' state of 'God.'

There is another application to Moshe. The word *mosh* means to feel, it is something tangible. We have just mentioned the ability to 'feel' darkness or chaos. At the opposite end, we know we can experience order for we do so every day. Moshe represents the complete spectrum of chaos and order for he was enveloped in both. In Egypt he was surrounded by chaos. Although superficially Egypt was very ordered, it was an artificially imposed order that resulted in imbalance and chaos. In the tent of meeting, he experienced complete order. In this case he may have experienced God's *kavod* which we just described as chaos but it was in perfect balance and harmony. Moshe is the archetypical man, just as Avraham was. A man's duty is to leave the chaos and seek the order.

The wind of the powers (*Elohim*) brooded over the creation like a mother hen broods over her nest of chicks. Here we have the powers, the land, and the water with the *ruach*/wind contemplating over them. The picture is not of an all powerful being separate from creation putting it all together like a scientist doing an experiment. It is more like a loving parent looking at a newborn baby and considering all the possibilities. The baby was created from its mother, it was nourished from her very being, it is a part of her. Creation developed in the same way; it is the essence of God's being.

'The Deep' itself is an interesting thing. The word here is *tahom*. This word is used in conjunction with several others in the scriptures. In Psalm 148:7 it is paralleled with the *tannim* which is a monster of some sort, probably something reptilian. In Job 26:12, 13 this 'monster' is both the *nechash* and *rahav*. In fact *tahom*, *rahav*, *leviathan*, *tannanim* and *nechash* are all used in parallel in the scriptures and are interchangeable. The roots of these words are *tom*, *tan*, *chash*, *rav*, and *latan*. *Tan* is to extend or stretch out. We know that *rav* is similar in meaning, something big. The *tannim* could be describing a very large reptile. Reptiles grow throughout their lives, hence the 'extending' or 'stretching.' It is interesting to note that in several ancient accounts of creation, the world was formed from a dead monster, often a dragon or snake, usually slain by one of the gods. The desire to put the abstract or unknowable into terms or stories that relate to our own experience is where such myths come from and is a fundamental drive of all peoples. It is taking these creation stories and assuming that they describe reality that cause misunderstanding, create religion and lead to disharmony among people and between people and the world around them.

Two more notes before we come back to our story. In Psalm 87:4 *rahav* is used as a parallel to Babylon and in Isaiah 30:7 it is paralleled with Egypt. These societies were identified with the chaos of creation and are used throughout the Bible when God wants to point out the opposite of what He desires. How does this relate to our story? Could it be that the world that preceded our creation account was so depraved it could be described this way? Much as ancient cities were destroyed and new ones built on top, often from the rubble, perhaps the world as we know it, is formed from the rubble of a past civilization so depraved it brought about the complete destruction of the known universe (or at least the Earth). Have we come close? Perhaps. When the first atomic bomb was detonated, scientists weren't sure what would happen and speculated on whether or not the atomic reaction started in the bomb would stop. It was thought that there was a possibility the atmosphere could 'burn up' or something else catastrophic would happen. Could we destroy our planet? The past says 'yes' but we have control over the when. May leaders of wisdom and patience rise up in the future to protect us and our universe from the selfish greed that leads to destruction. If not, there will be another civilization emerging from our chaos and wondering 'what happened before us?'

Genesis 1:3

וַיֹּאמֶר אֱלֹהִים יְהִי אוֹר וַיְהִי־אוֹר:

And he said, "the Powers be revealed by the light, and the light illuminated."

The 'he' in the beginning of the sentence is *Ayn Soph*. We use 'he' in translation rather than the more accurate 'it' to be true to Hebrew pronoun utilization which, unlike Greek or English, does not have a neuter; it has no 'it.' A simple explanation for the beginning here was that the first thing necessary was for *Ayn Soph* to see what it was doing. It had to 'turn on the lights.' It had to reveal the powers which will be divided into the sky and the land. The Hebrew word אר (*or*) means 'light' which we shall parallel with, and sometimes translate as, 'order.' The ancient pictograph for this word is ᛭ᛒ where the ᛒ represents strength and the ᛭ represents the head, the beginning, combined these pictographs mean 'strong beginning.' The jumbled up darkness, the unrealized potential, was beginning to be turned into energy. *Ayn Soph* is working and bringing order from the chaos. An expanded translation might say, "And *Ayn Soph* said, let there be a light to reveal the *Elohim*, and the light revealed." Chaos is nothing, it has no form and it is the light, the order that becomes something.

We again have a form of our verb *hayah* which we translate as 'reveal' and 'illuminate' to reflect the Hebrew parallelism, a poetic form in which a phrase or word is repeated in a different way but with similar meaning. A similar poetic structure emerges as we examine the whole story of creation as it is written like a poem. The separation of light and darkness on the first day parallels the creation of the sun, moon and stars on the fourth day. The separation of the waters and sky on the second day parallels the creation of the fish and birds on the fifth day. The appearance of the land on the third day corresponds to the creation of the animals and man on the sixth day.

This parallelism is significant. The sky and the land correspond to their obvious partners, which means that the powers parallel the light which parallels the sun and to a lesser extent, the moon and the stars. The sun is a 'direct' representation of *Elohim*. Malachi 3:21 refers to the 'sun of righteousness' in obvious reference to God. There are other significant parallels between God and the sun. One cannot look directly at the sun just as one cannot look on the face of God and live (Exodus 33:20). We can only look at the reflection or effect. The moon is a reflection of the sun and the creation is a reflection of God. God is responsible for all things in existence just as the sun is responsible for maintaining life on earth. We are admonished, however, in the Torah to worship no *Elohim* but YHVH. The ancients who engaged in sun worship failed to understand this important difference. The sun may be *Elohim* but it is not to be worshipped. Even that may be a difficult statement for many readers to comprehend or accept, but that is because as western thinkers we maintain a dualist mindset which differentiates the 'spiritual' from the 'physical.' The ancients made no such distinction. The sun, the land, the sky, they are all *Elohim* (both physical and spiritual) yet to treat them as 'superior beings' is to limit the true creative genius of the universe. *Ayn Soph* cannot be defined or limited to one mode of representation. Idolatry does just that. It takes one characteristic or representation of the force of creation and makes it into an object of worship. It may be the sun, the moon or a tree, it may be another object or another '*Elohim*' of creation or it may even be a man whom the scriptures also refer to as *Elohim*, such as Moshe. All are but parts of the whole and are an unworthy focus of worship and adoration. The Torah clearly states that the *Elohim* YHWH alone is to be worshiped. The Hebrew word for worship is *avod* and literally means 'to serve.' YHWH is the full representation of all the *Elohim*. We are to serve him, not the individual parts of *Elohim*.

Let's go a little deeper. Light is used in the Bible many times in many ways. It's most significant use comes from its use as a substitute for 'God.' As the scriptures say, "God is Light"[11]. Now when most western thinkers see that statement, we think that 'God is like light' or 'light is like God' or 'God emanates light.' This is our western minds imposing our dualistic way of looking at the world upon these passages. We believe God and the light are separate since 'God' is 'spiritual' and light is 'physical.' The fact is God *is* light and light *is* God. As modern physics studies light and its unique characteristics are continually revealed, its resemblance to our perception of 'God' continually grows.

Light is a unique phenomenon. It has characteristics of both waves and particles. Light is made up of 'things' we call photons. Going back to Isaac Newton, a photon was thought of as a particle. In our high school chemistry classes, most of us learned that sub-atomic particles, like electrons and protons, were like little 'balls' of matter and this was as small as we could go. Protons and neutrons make up the nucleus of an atom just as the sun is the center, nucleus, of our solar system. Electrons orbit the nucleus of an atom just as the planets orbit around the sun. Photons were thought of the same way. They were little balls moving very fast, 186,000 miles per second, in fact. The planetary model of the atom was simple to understand and all these little balls of matter moving at high speed were something we could easily visualize. The problem is, it doesn't work.

In the latter nineteenth century, a physicist named James Maxwell was doing some experiments with electromagnetism. In the process he

---

[11] See Psalm 27:1, Isaiah 60:20, Micah 7:8, I John 1:5

came to the realization that a self-reinforcing electromagnetic field, one which does not require magnets or electricity to produce or sustain it, has a speed equal to that of the speed of light. Therefore light must be an electromagnetic wave as opposed to a particle. He built on the work of Thomas Young who did an experiment that demonstrated the wave like properties of light. The experiment was simple. He put three boards in a row, one with one slit, the second with two and the third to see the projected light. It looked something like this;

Light Source
*

_____ _____

__ __ __

_____

The two slits in the experiment could each be covered with something. If only one slit was covered, the light went through and there was a diffused oval on the third board. This is similar to light coming through a window and being projected onto a wall in roughly the same shape as the window with the brightest area where the light comes directly in the window and a gradually diffused area of light around it. When both slits were opened one would expect two ovals on the projection sheet but that is not what happened at all. The wall was illuminated with alternating bands of darkness and light. The center band between the two slits was brightest and dark bands were on either side then two bands of slightly less light then dark bands etc. The key for him was that the light going through two slits interfered with one another just like *waves* do. One can see a similar effect at the ocean as waves go through narrow inlets or around several objects, they refract slightly and when they meet up they may cancel each other out if a crest meets a trough or amplify one another if a crest meets a crest. Light waves are the basis for many of the things we use everyday such as televisions and radios as well as in medical diagnosis-CAT scans, X-rays and procedures-lasers. Our own experience also tells us that light is 'massless.' It can be created by turning on a light and destroyed by turning it off. Particles don't do this. So Newton was wrong, right? Wrong.

Physicist Phillip Lenard in 1899 did some experiments that showed just the opposite. He shone light at a piece of metal and noticed how the photons, acting like little balls, knocked electrons out of their orbits at a certain energy level that corresponded with the wavelength of light used. A year later, Max Plank found that atoms could only absorb light in 'lumps' of certain sizes and calculated this amount exactly (called Plank's constant). Albert Einstein brought it all together by suggesting and mathematically supporting the idea that a beam of light of any frequency is really a stream of particles, photons, which have a certain amount of energy. He received the Nobel Prize for this work in 1921. So Newton was right after all? No.

As it turns out, everyone is right and light acts like both a wave and a particle, something rather confusing to our western minds. A particle is something defined by its location in space and whatever volume it may have. It is something real, something we can see, touch or taste or smell. Waves on the other hand, defy that kind of definition. They stretch on forever so there is no one point at which they exist. Yet light behaves like both of them at times. And to make things even more confusing, the behavior of light, and many other particles, depends on what we are looking for. If we are looking for light to behave as a particle, it will. But when we are not looking, it will behave like a wave. The reverse is also true. In a real sense, there is no objective experiment we can perform to describe light or any other elementary 'particle' as our objective affects the outcome. Easterners have always understood that there is no such thing as an 'objective' observer, that the process of observing something will always affect it in some way. Perspective is everything and everything is unified. But we learned that back in verse two. 'God' is both light and dark, good and evil. Now, because 'God' is *defined* as light, 'God' is both wave and particle. It all depends on our perspective and what we are looking for.[12]

Now there may be an important objection here. By defining God/light as a wave/particle, have we taken the 'intelligence' out of the universe? As a matter of fact, no. But one has to keep in mind that if we limit intelligence to *our* experience, what we think of as 'intelligence,' we are doing what the Bible itself warns against. "My ways are not your ways..."[13] God is so far beyond us, the definition of God's intelligence cannot be the same as ours. In fact, if we try to impose our ideas of intelligence, justice or logic on the God presented in the Bible, inconsistencies pop up everywhere, as we shall see as we proceed through Genesis.

Now let's bring Thomas Young's double slit experiment up to date and do it with single photons. Let's cover one slit and fire a proton at it. We will notice that it now hits the wall at a place where our previous experiment with two slits open was dark. We keep firing photons we will notice that the same diffused oval appears as in our first experiment. Now we open the second slit and fire one photon at a time. Now by firing one photon at a time there will be no interference for one needs two waves/particles to interfere with one another. Yet when we open both slits and fire one individual photon after another

---

[12] *The Search for Superstrings, Symmetry and the Theory of Everything* John Gribben, Little Brown and Company 1998 pp. 10-32
[13] Isaiah 55:8

(recording the results over time) we get the same bands of light and darkness as in our previous experiment. The only way this is possible is if the photon 'knows' that the other slit is open even if it did not go through it and although no other photon went through it at the same time to interfere with it, it acts as though there was. Does it 'know' that another photon went ahead of it and another will be coming behind and is therefore interfering with the memory or the future action of another photon? How did it get this information? Physicist E. H. Walker says, "Consciousness may be associated with all quantum mechanical processes. Since everything that occurs is ultimately the result of one or more quantum mechanical events, the universe is "inhabited" by an almost unlimited number of rather discrete conscious, usually non-thinking entities that are responsible for the detailed working of the universe.[14]" It is not that we have removed consciousness from the universe, it is just that it is a consciousness that operates in ways we do not understand and outside the bounds we normally impose on our own 'intelligence.'[15] This also means that if we can tune ourselves into this basic consciousness, the past and the future, as well as the present, the unity of all things will open themselves up to us.

Photons are also doing other things that we usually associate with 'God.' For example, we know that it is 'God' that provides the form and cohesion for the universe. We now know that photons are wave/particles and this definition can be applied to other sub-atomic entities as well. These sub-atomic 'fields' are divided into categories in several ways. One of them is into what are called pheromones and bosuns. The fields corresponding to pheromones (protons, neutrons,

---

[14] Evan Walker, "The Nature of Consciousness," Mathematical Biosciences, 7, 1970, pp. 175-176
[15] *The Dancing Wu Li Masters'* Gary Zukav Quill William Morrow, New York 1979 pp. 87, 88

electrons) produce what we know as the material world. The other kinds, corresponding to bosuns (photons, muons, pions) produce the interactions that hold the world together. Light and other related particles provide the cohesion and 'forces' that on a 'macro' level, make the world as we know it work.

Here is another example of this. The electron is not just a ball of something moving through space. The energy that constitutes it is constantly creating what are called 'virtual photons' which only move 1/2 their wavelength from the electron and are reabsorbed. (This would appear to violate the Einstienian idea that matter/energy can neither be created nor destroyed but that is another story.) The process of magnetism is now being explained by these 'virtual photons.' For example, when two electrons get close enough to each other they begin exchanging these photons and this exchange results in their repulsion. The photon leaves the first electron, pushing it back and the second electron absorbs the photon, moving in the opposite direction. One of the tasks of modern physics is the development of a theory that will explain all the forces (gravity, electromagnetism, strong and weak forces) into one package. The ideas surrounding light may provide some of the cohesion for such a theory.[16] For light is 'God' and 'God' is light and 'God' gives form and cohesion to the universe, then there is nothing in existence that will be explained or understood apart from 'God/light.'

---

[16] *The Search for Superstrings, Symmetry and the Theory of Everything* John Gribben, Little Brown and Company 1998 pp. 63, 64

Genesis 1:4

וַיַּרְא אֱלֹהִים אֶת־הָאוֹר כִּי־טוֹב וַיַּבְדֵּל אֱלֹהִים בֵּין הָאוֹר
וּבֵין הַחֹשֶׁךְ׃

The Powers saw the beauty of the light and he divided the Powers between the ordered light and the chaotic darkness.

This innocuous statement could be considered the defining verse of the entire Bible, it is the E=mc2 that describes the created order. If we can get our minds around it, this verse will go a long way towards giving us an understanding of, and peace with, the world we all would like to have. We will no longer be at odds with the world around us because of our incorrect assumptions and perceptions. It gives us an accurate picture of the Creator and defines how that Creator operates in the world. The world as it began is naturally chaotic, a mix of 'darkness' and 'light.' From this starting point *Ayn Soph* brings light and order into the chaos and darkness. The powers, *Elohim*, are bystanders in this verse yet are intimately involved. They *are* the light and the darkness. They are opposite yet complimentary. The division between the two is imposed by *Ayn Soph*, it is 'artificial.' God is both the restrainer/creator and the destroyer. This concept is perfectly illustrated in the story of Passover. YHVH is the one who goes throughout Egypt and strikes the firstborn[17], but it is also YHVH who stands at the door of the Israelite home and protects it from the destroyer[18]. The powers/*Elohim* are made up of chaos and order and

---

[17] Exodus 12:23 states, "For YHVH will pass through to strike the Egyptians..."

[18] Exodus 12:23 also states, "YHVH will not allow the destroyer to come into your houses to strike you."

are *echad*, a unity, and it is this unity that makes the created order what it is. We have been working toward this understanding of 'God' as the unifying force in all of creation, as light and darkness, good and evil. God is creation and encompasses all things. This verse makes clear what the previous verses have begun. Admittedly, this understanding of God is not what we all learned in Sunday School, but such an understanding will make a lot more sense, not only in making sense of the Bible but also in our daily lives. No longer will we live with a fickle God whom we cannot make sense of, who acts in ways that to us are unpredictable. Deep down don't we say, if I were God, I'd do.....whatever, you fill in the blank. That is because we think God is like us, only better. What we have seen so far says that God is nothing like us, yet is within us and all things. It has intelligence, but it is unlike ours. This may be unnerving to some but what follows is some more of the answer to what this unifying, creative force is really like.

Scientifically, this can be described by two opposing forces. The first is nucleic bonding or what physicists refer to as the 'strong force.' Every elementary school student knows that opposite magnetic poles attract and like poles repel. Within each atom there are at least two wave/particles in the old planetary model. A positive one called a proton and a negative one called an electron. Protons form the 'core' of the atom and the electrons orbit around them like the planets around the sun. Centrifugal force and magnetic attraction keep the electrons in 'orbit.' The problem comes when an atom contains more than one proton, all of which have a positive charge, and are grouped together in a clump called the nucleus. No one knows what keeps them bound together because they should naturally fly apart. Scientists call this phenomenon 'nucleic bonding' or the 'strong force.' The four major forces in the world-gravity, electromagnetism, and the strong and weak forces-simply are, they exist. Scientists can quantify them, understand their 'rules,' but as to what actually makes them work is still a mystery. We understand this as the imposition of *Ayn Soph*; it is the power that binds the world together. It is the presence of the divine in everything that exists. This constant action is necessary because of a second scientific law, the Second Law of Thermodynamics, which, as we stated earlier, basically states that all systems deteriorate over time if no new energy is introduced. This law tells us that the world would return to the primordial chaotic state if *Ayn Soph* would cease exercising its power.

The rest of the Bible, from this point forward, is the story of the imposed order vs. the underlying chaos. We have already described the cyclical nature of this deterioration and renewal. Paul says in II Thessalonians that there is a 'restrainer' that is taken away before the man of wickedness is revealed. Before the chaos of judgment, that which imposes order is taken away (the restrainer). Before the flood, man lived a lot longer and by applying the Second Law of Thermodynamics in a moral sense, he had a much longer lifespan to slide into evil and chaos, he had more time to become wicked. By limiting his life, God keeps man from becoming too evil if he chooses not to try to impose light (power) in his life. This is our duty, to reflect the light and order of the Creator in our lives and keep ourselves from sliding into chaos.

In the origin of creation, as we see in this verse, there was a balance between the order and chaos; they were in harmony, in *shalom*. The amount of energy being infused into creation offset the trend to chaos, and things were living and growing properly without a constant deterioration. That is why it was 'good.' We have translated *tov* as beauty because to the ancient Hebrew mind, that which functions properly is beautiful. With proper balance between the *Elohim* of light and the *Elohim* of darkness, between the imposed order and underlying chaos, everything was working as it was supposed to.

This discussion of *Elohim* or 'God' as 'darkness' may be problematic to some yet we know there is a negative and a positive to all things, scientifically, morally, spiritually, etc. Our dualistic western mind sees the negatives as bad and to be avoided or eliminated. We see the positives as good and to be accepted or sought. The eastern mind sees the negatives and positives as the two necessary ingredients for balance, or *shalom*. In a magnet there are positive and negative charges yet we do not assign moral value to either one. They are necessary components of the whole. In the same way, darkness is negative and light is positive. Both are necessary for perfect *shalom*. Pure darkness is chaos resulting in blindness. Pure light is also chaos as it brings blindness. Only by a balance of the two can one see.

The world of quantum physics has substantiated this idea that at the most basic level of creation there is chaos, that things operate by pure 'chance' (which is what made Einstein reject many of the ideas of quantum mechanics). In our last verse we saw that photons and other elementary 'particles' have the characteristics of both waves and particles. If we want to 'find' a particle that is like a wave, we have to confine the wave somehow, we have to take a pure, infinite wave and limit it. Through something called Fourier analysis we can produce a combination of waves that cancel each other out except for in specifically designed regions of space called a wave packet. If it could be made small enough, the location of a single photon or electron could be found. But to do so, the particle's unique wavelength, that which gives it direction and momentum, has been corrupted to the point where knowledge of where it will be next is very uncertain. The point of this is that by knowing more about a particle's location, we know less about its momentum and direction. The more we know about direction and momentum, the less we know about location. It is impossible to know both the location and momentum of a sub-atomic particle with precision. Because of this uncertainty we cannot know the direction or location of a particle and therefore we cannot know where it will be from one moment to the next.

This is not the only uncertain relationship in the world of subatomic particles. The relationship between time and energy is just as uncertain. The more we know about time, the less we know of energy and vice versa. For example, a particle may have a certain range of energy at a given moment but it could 'find' the energy to break out of an orbit or escape the nucleus or any number of unpredictable or unusual things. Another example would be the path a particle takes to get from point A to point B. The Newtonian concept of such a situation would be that the particle would follow a trajectory determined by velocity, gravity and direction, among other things. The reality is, however, that a wave/particle will follow any number of paths from A to B and there is only a certain probability that it will follow any one of them. The reality of things at the subatomic level is that there is a lot of uncertainty and the behavior of any one wave/particle is governed completely by chance. While groups of particles generally behave in certain ways (probability), enough so that the world we live in is rather predictable, the underlying structure is uncertain and chaotic.[19]

Does this idea of chance and probability work on the 'macro' level, in the world we see and experience? For a long time science said no. All things work according to physical laws we can discover and understand. Anything 'unexplained' was relegated to the realm of pseudoscience. Weird happenings, things some call 'miraculous,' were swept under the rug, not talked about by serious and educated people. But what if the uncertainty of the quantum level does govern our lives here in the world we can see? What if I ran myself into a solid

---

[19] *The Search for Superstrings, Symmetry and the Theory of Everything* John Gribben, Little Brown and Company 1998 pp. 33-43

wall enough times (several billion) to find that one odd occurrence in probability that I would go through it rather than bounce off it. If one billion people have some fatal disease over a certain period of time and 99% die do we not say the lucky 1% experienced a miracle? Now on our level, the probabilities of a certain course of action are very great, most likely, greater than a billion to one. But with 5 billion people on the planet and a nearly infinite combination of circumstances surrounding each one, the likelihood of odd things happening, of people experiencing the very small probabilities happening, becomes much more likely. Even more intriguing is the idea that perhaps we can put the odds more in our favor, that there are things we can do to increase the likelihood of the small probabilities and 'perform miracles.'

You may have read all of this and wondered what the big deal is, why was this verse so crucial, how does it help me now? Think harder. We have eliminated dualism, the idea that there is a separation between the physical and spiritual. We have dethroned a personal God and expanded the idea of God to an intelligence unlike ours that is both infinitely transcendent and intimately connected with all things. We have stated that light and dark, evil and good are both interwoven in the fabric of God and creation. We have come to understand that the world on the micro/quantum level is chaotic and governed apparently by chance and probability and ultimately that may be the case in our reality as well. So how do we look at the world, our place in it and what do we look for when we ask moral and religious questions.

First, we must recognize that the ultimate objective is to bring about harmony and balance between all things. For example, natural processes are not good and evil; they are just the natural world's way of maintaining balance. We look on such things as evil when we have surrounded ourselves with an artificial order that is in conflict with the natural order. An earthquake in a major city is usually seen as a bad thing. The earthquake itself is simply the earth restoring balance where there was tension. The loss of life comes from people creating an artificial environment, a city, in a place where these things are likely to happen. If everyone lived in tents like the nomads of Avraham's time and an earthquake happened, the losses would be minimal. When tall buildings and bridges and other manmade structures collapse, the losses in life and property are much greater and we think it is bad. A religious person may even postulate it was the judgment of God. It was no such thing. It was the earth doing what it does and people suffering the consequences of creating an artificial order at odds with the natural one.

During the dust bowl of the 1930s, a severe drought occurred in the prairies of the United States and Canada that completely wiped out the crops and dried out the soil. When the winds blew, it picked up this soil and carried for miles as dark clouds of dust, sometimes taking it as far as the Atlantic Ocean. This event wreaked havoc on the inhabitants of the area, not only by destroying their crops, but literally burying them in dust. In record numbers these people went to their churches and prayed to God to deliver them from what they believed to be a natural catastrophe. What these farmers did not realize at the time was that they had completely upset the balance of that region and they themselves created the catastrophe. In its natural state, the prairies were covered with native grasses that covered the soil. The leaves of these grasses shaded the soil keeping the moisture in the soil and its roots held the soil in place. When people began to farm this land they removed all the native grasses upsetting this balance and when the drought struck the area, the barren soil quickly dried out and was blown away by the winds.

The eastern mind understands these natural processes and tries to live in harmony with it while the western mind seeks to impose an artificial order and insulate itself from the natural world. The farther we insulate ourselves from the natural world, the more catastrophic the results when our artificial construct meets the irresistible corrective force of the universe. Death is a part of life, part of the natural cycle of things. In the west, we do our best to insulate ourselves from it and avoid it at all costs. It is devastating when someone close to us experiences it because it is so foreign to us. In the east, and in the Bible, death is seen as part of life. When the patriarchs die it is with final blessings for their families in a serene environment.

Perhaps this contrast between eastern and western thought in this respect is a bit misleading when discussing this idea of natural vs. artificial and the desire to be in harmony with each other and the world around us. It is more a contrast between the nomad and the city-state. The nomadic lifestyle was a simple one whose footprint on the world around him was very small. His possessions were very limited; he had to be able to move them with ease. He used only those resources that were necessary for life and his leisure was simple. He was attuned to the natural world around him, he had to be. The weather, the fauna, even the animals needed to be read and understood, his life was dependent on it. He could adapt easily because he was mobile and adaptable. The primary social unit was the family, immediate and extended. He was free, but also ultimately responsible for his own safety and survival.

The city-state, in contrast, was a social unit made up of many unrelated individuals who sacrificed their freedom for the apparent safety of numbers and the means of protection they could fabricate. Their primary loyalty, and their firstfruits, belonged to the city-state (government) and not themselves or their family. They were, by their very nature, static; physically and spiritually. Physically, because they built permanent structures. Their footprint in the world becomes much larger in terms of resources used (and wasted). In times of drought or crisis they couldn't easily pick up and move to greener pastures. They also had more 'stuff' because, as we know through experience, the longer one stays in one place the more one accumulates and the more one becomes attached to the accumulated things. The decision that 'we can't live without it' may just lead to that result. Lot's wife comes to mind. City people also become specialized in the division of labor. In a crisis, this means that the community will be unable to do some important things if the specialists (like the food producers or warriors) are no longer available.

Spiritually, used in the broadest sense, they also become static. They are not easily adaptable to new ways of thinking or doing because the monotony of their surroundings and daily lives dulls their ability to change. 'We've always done it this way.' Cult religion forms in this environment, usually as a way for a certain person or group to maintain political control leading to slavery of the populace. As the population grew other problems arose. Sanitation becomes a problem. People living in close proximity spread disease easily. The desire to accumulate leads to greed which leads to war.

Our western society, whose methods and values have spread across the globe, is the epitome of this and its problems are magnified. Our footprint had lead to environmental catastrophes in many places. The production of so much useless stuff creates so much waste. We live anonymously in a world completely dependent on technology. The same technology that results in disease we never knew and a level of government oppression never before possible. If the plug was ever pulled, if literally there was no electricity for example, the vast majority of the people in western style societies would be dead within a few weeks. Do you know how to provide food for yourself outside of a grocery store? Do you know how to protect yourself and your family from the total social meltdown that would result? Could you mentally adapt to a life without instant communication or money? What about shelter? These are things we think we have a 'right' to in our society, someone is responsible for making sure we have the things we need and it isn't us - it's society (government). Will it happen? At some point, nothing lasts forever. Ask the Egyptians, Romans, Spaniards, the British or the Chinese. The disharmony that we have produced from the creation of this artificial world will be corrected. The prophets foretell as much. The question is, will you be ready?

How should we then live, physically and spiritually? Physically, we should live simply. We are not the sum total of our possessions and we should not bring our children up to be even more lavish consumers than we are. We should eat simply and avoid so many of the health consequences of being so far removed from the earth's production. We should learn how to provide the basic necessities and how to protect ourselves. If you can't live nomadically, develop a nomadic mindset. Be free and independent; don't use society as a crutch. Live in harmony with the world around you.

Spiritually, our ultimate goal becomes relational, not religious. When we seek answers to moral and religious question we no longer seek to apply outdated rules or ideas but we seek that which brings harmony and balance in relationships. If we ask ourselves what will bring about the most harmony in our lives and the lives of others, we will always do the correct moral action and the consequences will be good. Creating disharmony results in anger, pain, and guilt and depending on the act, physical disease or death. It is the restoration of balance in nature and relationships that will bring about harmony and make life what is was meant to be. `

Genesis 1:5

וַיִּקְרָא אֱלֹהִים לָאוֹר יוֹם וְלַחֹשֶׁךְ קָרָא לָיְלָה וַיְהִי־עֶרֶב
וַיְהִי־בֹקֶר יוֹם אֶחָד:

**And he called the Powers for order "light" and for chaos he
called "darkness." And there were Powers for watching chaos
and Powers for illuminating order, a unified work in chaos.**

Once the division of the *Elohim* had been accomplished, *Ayn Soph*
places a name on them. This is not simply a label as names are today.
When ancient cultures ascribed a name to something, that name
encompassed the object's character and function. We see this in the
Bible over and over. People's names in the Bible had meaning, often
describing some aspect of God's plan. Note what is being named-the
Elohim. There are *Elohim* that bring order and there are *Elohim*
associated with chaos. The words *boqer*-morning and *erev*-evening
both have the letters ℜ (*resh*) and ט (*beyt*) which combined mean
'head of the house.' This head of the house is God/*Elohim*. The letter
𝓟 (*qoph*) in *boqer* is a picture of the sun rising above the horizon,
hence 'illumination.' The letter ◉ (*ayin*) in *erev* is symbolic of the eye,
something that sees, hence 'watching.' There is a parallel here
between watching and illuminating, between that which is seen and
the one that sees. Chaos that which watches is passive. Illumination,
which requires energy, is active. You may see an association between
the yin/yang idea in eastern cultures and this is not a bad thing. As
stated previously, the Semitic people have much more in common
with the eastern way of thinking than with the Greco-Roman west.
Throughout this chapter of Genesis, as well as the rest of the Bible,
you will see this idea of unity in separation again and again.

The word אור (or - meaning light) is another important word in the translation. It points to the author of order in the universe. The Hebrew word *or* is made up of the characters *aleph* (𐤀 in the ancient pictographic script) and *resh* (𐤓 in the ancient pictographic script). As has been previously stated, the aleph is a pictograph of a bull, something strong. The *resh* is a man's head, the first, the beginning. 'Or' then is the strong beginning which refers back to verse one in which the beginning was identified as *Ayn Soph*. The Beginning (*Ayn Soph*) is working to bring order. The light and order permeating all of creation to varying degrees is due to the activity of *Ayn Soph* and we could say, as we have previously, is *Ayn Soph*.

This day is not called the 'first' day, as the other days are numbered. If it was to be the 'first' day the Hebrew would have been *rishon*. Instead, the writer used *echad*, a unity. It is a unity of all things; all days are encompassed in this one. This one verse is paralleled to all the other days of creation. Even in the apparent separation that is part of this day, and will be part of all the days that follow, everything in the universe is *echad*, a unity. Light and darkness are unified; one cannot have one without the other. The order and the chaos are unified; one is unrecognizable without the other. Light and darkness, order and chaos, life and death, good and evil, are encompassed within *Elohim* and *Elohim* is *Echad*. When we talk about God being one/*echad*/unity, even in the *sh'ma*[20], we need to remember this. Separation is an illusion and it is when we see things as separate that pride and fear begin to rule our lives rather than *shalom*.

Let's explore this a little further. We can see that the interactions between people, and between people and the world around them, are influenced by this idea. If I see you as separate from me I can easily objectify you and if I can objectify you, I can treat you as 'equipment' rather than something that has inherent value. By objectifying individuals or groups, we can use and abuse them under the delusion that it does not affect us. We see the world in terms of I/us and him/them and life becomes a competition in a zero sum game. We soon accept our role as a persecutor or the persecuted depending on whether we are taking or giving a limited amount of resources, roles that may change for us day by day and even moment by moment. Our idea of 'God' suffers as well because in a sense he becomes the greatest persecutor, the ultimate distributor of resources and in our self interest we attempt to do what we think will please Him, feeling guilty when his all seeing eye catches us in a moment of disloyalty. All conflict, whether between individuals or nations, can be traced to this ability to objectify people or groups.

The opposite of this is to see all things as unified and interrelated. There is nothing I do that does not have an effect on the world around me and therefore I must be conscious of my impact. Every word that I use, every action I take has consequences for good or evil, to create harmony or disharmony, many of which I may be unaware of. And not only do these things affect the world and people around me, they affect *me*. Even the most self-absorbed person does not wish to create problems for himself. So if I think about the short and long term consequences of my words and actions on myself, and the world around me, with the understanding that no action happens in a vacuum, I will be careful about my impact. I will treat every person with dignity and respect because they are me, we are *echad*/unified, and everything I do affects both of us. I will treat the natural world with respect because we are one with it. If I abuse it, it will have

---

[20] Deuteronomy 6:5 - 'Hear' O Israel. The word 'hear' is the Hebrew word *sh'ma*.

negative consequences for me. 'God' is also in this unity, I am not separate from 'Him' or 'He' from me. We now work in partnership just as we should work in partnership with the people and the world around us. To what purpose? To bring *shalom* and harmony to all things.

There is much speculation concerning the meaning of a 'day' in the Genesis account. Instead of translating *yom* as day, we have expanded it according to its ancient paleographic Hebrew meaning. The *yad* (ﭏ) is a hand that works, the *vav* (Y) is a connector, a nail, and the *mem* (ﻣ) is water/chaos. Each day then, is a work in chaos; it is bringing order out of chaos. Each day encompasses all that is necessary for life. On this planet, water is the basis for life and light provides the energy that makes it possible. Creation begins with chaos/water and when work is done, energy is added, light and heat are produced. The basic building blocks for all that follow are now in place.

Now all this sounds nice and neat, 'a unified work in chaos,' as if something real has been created. 'Real' being defined as something that we can see or touch. We can 'see' light and we can 'feel' water. This is a simplistic view of the text because that is not what is being talked about here. We need to go deeper, much deeper. So deep, as a matter of fact, that the reality we think we know ceases to exist. The fact is that at the subatomic level, *there is nothing there that we know of that actually exists.* For example, the laws of quantum physics allow for (and some mathematical equations require) what are called virtual particles. Some of these are photons created and absorbed within atoms themselves, some are particle/anti-particle pairs that exist only for very short periods of time. Physicists like Paul Davies propose that the particles we talk about-photons, neutrons, electrons and the like, do not actually exist. We cannot see, feel or touch such things. All we can do is carry out experiments, observe the results and make conclusions and develop theories about what we can actually see. We can do things to them to see how they react but really we know nothing about the world of sub-atomic particles. As ideas and theories are developed and worked on and the flaws are revealed, it should not be surprising that the flaws are there, but that the theories work at all.

This idea that there is no underlying reality as we think of reality may seem ridiculous but it is actually the majority view of physicists today and for the last hundred years. There is what is called the Copenhagen interpretation of quantum physics proposed by Neils Bohr of the Copenhagen Institute. Bohr claims that there is no deep reality. The world around us is real enough but it is superimposed on a world that is not real. Bohr said "there is no quantum world. There is only an abstract quantum description." Werner Heisenberg, one of the founders of quantum physics said, "The hope that new experiments will lead us back to objective events in time and space is about as well founded as the hope of discovering the end of the world in the unexplored regions of the Antarctic." John Wheeler also added "No elementary phenomenon is a real phenomenon until it is an observed phenomenon."[21] We will look at this last statement in depth when we get to the creation of man.

One way of looking at it from a realist perspective, the one Albert Einstein ascribed to, is to see 'particles' as the states of energy that exist between interactions. At the subatomic level there are no real 'things,' just fields of energy and it is these fields and their interactions and combinations that give rise to 'particles.' Einstein said in his famous equation that mass and energy are two states of the same 'thing.' This 'thing' or energy field is not smooth like a wave but comes in specific 'lumps' of a definite quantity (hence quanta). Particles

---

[21] *Quantum Reality* Nick Herbert, Anchor Press, New York 1985 pp. 16-18

represent the quantities of these fields, but the fields are not little pieces of mass. The universe is really made up, not of these tiny pieces of matter, but of energy fields that interact with one another in an elaborate dance.

For the vast majority of the population that knows little of physics and assumes that the world we see is made up of progressively smaller bits of matter (compounds> molecules> atoms> sub-atomic particles) the idea that the smaller things on the list don't actually exist is a little odd. It really isn't too hard to believe, however. Most religious people believe that the 'reality' that lies under everything we see and know is 'God,' however defined. In our treatment of the subject, we may label this reality *"Ayn Soph."* Whether approached scientifically or through the vehicle of faith, the result is the same. We really don't know and *cannot know* what the fundamental basis for our world is. It is and will always remain a mystery.[22]

---

[22] *The Search for Superstrings, Symmetry and the Theory of Everything* John Gribben, Little Brown and Company 1998 pp. 55-56

Genesis 1:6

וַיֹּאמֶר אֱלֹהִים יְהִי רָקִיעַ בְּתוֹךְ הַמָּיִם וִיהִי מַבְדִּיל בֵּין
מַיִם לָמָיִם:

**And he said the Powers will spread out a sheet through waters.
And he caused a separating out of the waters to waters.**

A new creative agent is now introduced. The Powers (*Elohim*), at the direction of *Ayn Soph* (He), now begin to take an active part in the fabrication of the known universe. We will see that throughout the creative process, different agents are employed at the discretion of *Ayn Soph* to actually do the work of creating. *Ayn Soph*, being 'Nothing' and 'Everything' is the force behind and within all creation and the raw material/energy from which it is made. Therefore, *Ayn Soph* is not and cannot be the fashioner of that material/energy as we think of it. *Ayn Soph* is not the potter, *Ayn Soph* is more like the potter's employer (and the clay at the same time!) and we shall see that there are several potters in the creative process. This cohesive and directive process is necessitated by what is called Bell's Theorem. In order to explain the experimental facts of quantum experiments, John Bell believed that there is an invisible field directing superluminal information among all the parts of the universe. To understand this, we must define two different realities. The first is what Bell called non-local which is what we perceive and classical physics supports. It is the world we experience every day. In this reality, nothing that can transmit information can travel faster than light, which has time travel implications, incidentally. Local reality, on the other hand, means that everything in the universe is intimately connected and the communication of information occurs, super-luminally, faster than light.[23] *Ayn Soph* is the label we put on this 'field' that is the facilitator for all that happens in the universe. It is this local reality that gives rise to the phenomenon of prophesies, for example. If one can learn to experience reality on the local level, one will have information available from anywhere at any time. There will be no limits. Instead of looking at the universe and history as linear, time and reality become a web that is woven together and can be traveled on in any number of directions.

The previous verse revealed these creative agents, the 'powers,' and they now begin ordering the chaos that is the universe. There is an interesting pattern to be observed. The major work of God is that of separation yet all that exists is *echad*, in union with God. The separation is an illusion for all is made of the stuff of God and it is our western mindset that equates chaos/darkness with something bad. The universe could not exist without it.

The powers in our verse separate the chaos with a 'sheet,' the *rakiah*[24]. When *rakiah* is translated this way it is analogous to the 'sheet' of gold over the ark. The gold enclosed the ark, separating what was inside from everything outside. The holy things inside the ark represent of the kingdom and the gold *rakiah* separates the kingdom from the chaos outside. The curtain in the holy of holies separates what is behind the curtain from the uncleanness/chaos outside. The *rakiah* in our universe does the same thing; it separates the holy/order from the chaos outside. In order for the amount of organization required for building atomic and molecular compounds, not to mention more complex organisms, most of the chaos that made up the universe had to be kept out of our world. The *rakiah* formed a

---

[23] *Quantum Reality* Nick Herbert, Anchor Press, New York 1985 pp. 51-52

[24] From the root *raka* meaning 'to hammer a metal into a sheet' (see Exodus 39:3).

barrier between the vast chaos outside and the small amount left on this earth.

This amount of chaos or randomness is necessary. For example, we need free radicals to make up many of the molecular compounds. The Hebrew word for blood is **דם** (*dam*) where the original pictographs of this word represent a door (ᗡ) and water/chaos (ᗡ) therefore; *dam* is the 'door to chaos.' Blood, as well as our bodies, is made up of a large percentage of water/chaos and it is this chaos that carries the breath of God that brings life to our bodies. There isn't a pattern as to which cells get oxygen from the blood at which time yet all the cells receive it, a balance of chaos and order to achieve a good result. When it is inside the body and everything is in balance, it works rather well providing all the necessities of life to every cell in our body. Outside the body, it is pure chaos, it is unclean. Water/chaos makes up much of the earth and is necessary for life. There is a delicate balance between this chaos and order that, when upset, results in disaster. Free radicals in our bodies cause damage just as moral chaos results in judgment. Up to the time of the flood, for instance, men were constantly introducing more and more chaos into the world. They did this morally and physically through the shedding of blood. The *rakiah*, the waters above, broke down and introduced a much larger amount of chaos into the world as a flood, a consequence we still live with. Our shortened life spans are a testament to this fact. The same thing happened with the Amalakites. God told Avraham that their iniquity was not yet 'full,' the land was not ready to vomit them out quite yet. This is a testament to God's mercy. But when that mercy is up, the laws of cause and effect take over and balance is restored through the release of all that excess chaos. However, even the judgment is an act of mercy. By bringing chaos upon the chaotic, God makes the way for a new order to be created within the succeeding generation.

Genesis 1:7

וַיַּעַשׂ אֱלֹהִים אֶת־הָרָקִיעַ וַיַּבְדֵּל בֵּין הַמַּיִם אֲשֶׁר מִתַּחַת לָרָקִיעַ וּבֵין הַמַּיִם אֲשֶׁר מֵעַל לָרָקִיעַ וַיְהִי־כֵן:

And the Powers spread out the sheet separating out the waters from the bottom side belonging to the sheet and separating the water out from the top side belonging to the sheet. And he stood firm.

In this verse the actual separating takes place. The *rakiah* (the sheet) is spread out[25] between the upper part, the canopy above, from the lower part, from the bottom of the ocean to the *rakiah*. The *rakiah* itself represents the entire ordered universe from chaos to order or *shalom*. To make this clearer, and to avoid the misconceptions we have about the words chaos and order and the moral connotations we may ascribe them, we will introduce two Hebrew terms, ᴹ✝ (*tam*) and ✝ᴹ (*mot*), for the extremes of the continuum. '*Tam*,' perhaps more familiar in the form *tamiym* (perfect), is the word we will use to describe the part of the continuum that encompasses the idea of order, *shalom*, wholeness; that which is functional. In the ancient Hebrew pictographs, it is a ✝ (the letter *tav* - a mark) and a ᴹ (the letter *mem* - chaos). In *tam*, the mark of God is before/over the chaos. It is the opposite with '*mot*,' the other term we will use. *Mot* is a ᴹ (*mem*) and a ✝ (*tav*). In this case the chaos is over the mark meaning that death, chaos, and dysfunction are the overriding characteristics. Again, these are not moral terms but descriptive ones. A living tree is *tam* and a dead rotting one is *mot* but that *mot* tree is giving life and

---

[25] The Hebrew verb translated as 'spread out' is *asah* literally meaning 'to do' and is another of the generic verbs which can be used in a wide range of applications.

order to other organisms and maybe even its progeny. Each one has a function in bringing harmony to the earth, the live one providing oxygen and the dead one, fertilizer.

In the previous verse, 'He' (*Ayn Soph*) tells *Elohim* to spread out the *rakiah* and in this verse we see *Elohim* doing just that. The fact that the *Elohim* are doing the creating here is not lost in the pages of the rest of the scriptures. Psalm 150:1 "Praise the LORD! Praise God in his sanctuary; praise him in his mighty firmament" and Psalm 19:1 "The heavens are telling the glory of God; and the firmament proclaims his handiwork." *Elohim* are that which we know in this world, that small part of the infinite we can partake of. *Elohim* is analogous to the sheet itself and encompasses everything from *tam* to *mot* and the ordered state those two opposites represent. The universal order is really a combination of *tam* and *mot*. Order is not the absence of *mot* but an ordered balance of *tam* and *mot*. *Elohim* (God) is made up of this balance of *tam* and *mot*.

There is a word that brings this unity of things in order together. The word *asher*, in its original ancient meaning it has the idea of a rope that brings together that which was before and that which is after. The *rakiah*, while separating the waters is also a part of them. In some sense, it belongs to them.

Finally 'He stood firm.' The 'he' in this case is *Ayn Soph*; the he again is used because there is no neuter in Hebrew. *Ayn Soph* is the power that underlies everything and it is 'his' firmness on which the created order stands.

Genesis 1:8

וַיִּקְרָא אֱלֹהִים לָרָקִיעַ שָׁמָיִם וַיְהִי־עֶרֶב וַיְהִי־בֹקֶר יוֹם
שֵׁנִי׃

And he called the Powers belonging to the sheet "sky." And there were Powers for watching chaos and Powers for illuminating order, a second work in chaos.

This verse illustrates the previous point that *Elohim*, the powers, are distinct from *Ayn Soph* and are part of the creation itself. The powers 'belong' to the sheet which represents the order of the universe from *tam* to *mot*. There are *Elohim* that are part of the *rakiah* that are passive, they 'watch the chaos' and there are *Elohim* that are active by 'illuminating order.' *Ayn Soph*, to illustrate his authority and power, name the *Elohim*, because in ancient Hebrew culture, naming something demonstrated authority over it.

The first day the powers were unified in the work, and now the powers are separated and work is delegated among them. Therefore, instead of a unified work, we now have a *second* work. There is another implication to this idea. With the understanding that it is not a day but a work in chaos, the days are not necessarily in order and will support alternative groupings, avoiding the controversy surrounding the origins of the universe. Much arguing has been done over the meaning of a 'day' and one of the fundamental disagreements between science and religion concerns the methods by which creation was accomplished and, by implication, how long it took. It is the opinion of these authors that there is no conflict between science and religion and the conflict only arises when science moves into the realm of theology and meaning when trying to understand the implications of physical phenomenon, or when religion holds onto theological ideas that fly in the face of observable and verifiable scientific data.

In reality, science and religion have two different goals. Science tries to explain what and how, while religion is concerned with the why and what for. Science is concerned with objective verifiable fact, and religion is concerned with subjective experience. Science is constantly moving forward as new discoveries revolutionize our way of understanding the world around us. It constantly acquires and seeks to explain new information. Religion, on the other hand, often looks backward. It seeks to recapture and understand revelation which is by its very nature, subjective, because it is concerned only with the individual. In science the observer is a corrupting influence, in religion the individual is all that matters. Yet the two are very close. When science finds the answer to the 'what,' the 'why' naturally follows. When we read the Bible it may give us the answer to 'why' but we then wonder 'how.' The creation story was not witnessed by anyone. Moshe may have written it based on traditions that could go back to Adam but even he did not see it. The creation account is not primarily a scientific account, although to be a true religion it cannot contradict science. We have sought to demonstrate how even modern science is found within the Genesis account. This account is an attempt to explain not primarily the observable world but the unity of all dimensions of reality and our place within them. As such, the Book of Genesis is a brilliant piece of very accurate work where every word and character, and even the cultural context from which it grew, contribute to its multi-layered explanation.

Genesis 1:9

וַיֹּאמֶר אֱלֹהִים יִקָּווּ הַמַּיִם מִתַּחַת הַשָּׁמַיִם אֶל־מָקוֹם
אֶחָד וְתֵרָאֶה הַיַּבָּשָׁה וַיְהִי־כֵן:

And he said, "The Powers will gather and watch the waters from under the skies move toward one place and dry land will be presented." And he stood firm.

In this verse there is another creative agent introduced. In the beginning there was *Ayn Soph* who got everything started. Then the powers began arranging things in order, but now the powers themselves become spectators, they are the ones doing the watching. Now the earth itself becomes one of the creative partners. *Ayn Soph* appears to be ordering the world in a very specific way, a way that does not require constant attention to every detail. It is what we might call delegation of responsibility. *Ayn Soph* is the founder of this company called the universe; it is the 'idea man.' The powers are like the vice presidents in charge of various areas of enterprise and now we have introduced 'middle management. *Ayn Soph* provides the raw material and patterns for everything but these 'lesser' agents are actually doing the ordering, arranging and separating.

The thing that is actually doing the work in our verse is the water/chaos. It is imposing limitations on itself and revealing the dry land. Chaos, as we have said before, has a crucial role to play in the workings of the universe and it takes an active part in its ordering. It is part of the order itself, coexisting and participating in the operation of the universe. This is vital to understand. Perfect order is not the goal nor is it possible in our world. That goes for all realms of human and scientific endeavor. Even though we may be able to predict certain outcomes scientifically (i.e. the flight of spacecraft or medical treatment) with a degree of reliability that is acceptable to us, absolute precision is a myth. There is always uncertainty because there are an infinite set of variables in every equation. In the 'real' world, they may not matter much because they are not small enough to negatively affect the outcome (i.e. a spacecraft will come down in a certain defined area) but it is there.

In human systems such as psychology, sociology and economics, for example, the chaos inherent in the systems becomes even more obvious and our ignorance of it more catastrophic. In socialistic or communist systems, perfect order and conformity is the goal and regardless of the methods used to achieve it, it will fail because the goal is unattainable. Each person in a system adds exponentially to the chaos and in a nation of millions that really adds up! Human beings are free people and though we may think them generally predictable (society or civilization is based on that assumption) sooner or later we all make choices that are outside the box. When our lives become too ordered we feel constricted. When we no longer feel in control, that all our decisions are being made for us, we try to take some of that control back. Since our egos, other people's expectations of us, and our economic security do not allow us to change our basic circumstances-quit our jobs, change our living situation-we choose to take control in other ways that allow some measure of chaos in our lives. This usually entails activities with some kind of risk (uncertainty-chaos) associated with them. It may be something relatively benign like game playing or amusement park rides or it may come out in more destructive behaviors like reckless driving, sexual conquest, alcohol abuse or drug use. The most extreme case would be the individual that lashed out suddenly and hurts or kills people, generally those close to him or her that they perceive as causing their suffocating situation. The new articles usually go something like, "He was such a nice man, good job, nice house, pretty wife and good children. Why would he suddenly lash out and kill her/them?" There is, no doubt, an inverse relationship between the lack of chaos allowed by a society (or individual) and the degree of chaotic behavior engaged in by those within the society.

Genesis 1:10

וַיִּקְרָא אֱלֹהִים לַיַּבָּשָׁה אֶרֶץ וּלְמִקְוֵה הַמַּיִם קָרָא יַמִּים
וַיַּרְא אֱלֹהִים כִּי־טוֹב:

And he called the Powers belonging to the dry ground "land,"
and he called the waters belonging to the collection, "sea."
And the Powers saw the beauty.

In this verse two things are named. The first is the 'dry ground' or *yabashah*, the second being the 'collection' or *mikveh*. These two words give us the two basic forces at work in the universe. If we describe the ancient meaning of the word *yabashah*, utilizing the ancient pictographs - ᠊᠊ meaning hand or work, ᠊᠊ meaning house or dwelling, ᠊᠊ meaning teeth or press and ᠊᠊ meaning behold, we end up with something like 'behold the pressing work on the dwelling.' This is the work of order, organization. In contrast to the chaotic fluidity of the ocean, dry land is organized; it is divided into climate, terrain and ecosystems of infinite variety.

The other word is *mikveh* which denotes a collection of something. Its pictographic meaning from the letters ᠊᠊ meaning water/chaos, ᠊᠊ meaning sunrise or rising, ᠊᠊ meaning nail or connector and ᠊᠊ meaning behold, is something like 'Behold the rising connective chaos.' Nothing on this planet lives without water and water is descriptive of chaos. We usually think of using order to bind things together but it is really chaos that unifies the infinite 'islands' of order throughout the universe.

The gathered waters is called *yam*, spelled ᠊᠊ in the original pictographic script, is a 'working chaos' or chaos that works-doing the work of unification. The 'dry land' is called *eretz* or the 'first head of the hunt' from the letters ד meaning first, ר meaning head and ף meaning hunt, the hunt or pursuit of order.

Genesis 1:11

וַיֹּאמֶר אֱלֹהִים תַּדְשֵׁא הָאָרֶץ דֶּשֶׁא עֵשֶׂב מַזְרִיעַ זֶרַע עֵץ
פְּרִי עֹשֶׂה פְּרִי לְמִינוֹ אֲשֶׁר זַרְעוֹ־בוֹ עַל־הָאָרֶץ וַיְהִי־כֵן:

And he said, "Powers bring forth young green plants on the land. Sow seed of fruit trees, producing fruit for its continuing its offspring whose seed is in it all over the land." And he stood firm.

The powers here are the powers of the previous verse associated with the 'dry land.' In case you are having a problem accepting a multitude of creative agents as opposed to one, i.e. 'God,' even the translators of all modern English translations have the earth as the creative agent in this verse when they state "Let the earth bring/put forth grass/vegetation...."

Everything is now in place to begin producing life. The water/chaos had been established in its proper role as the connector/unifier that will now allow the forces of order, the *yabashah* called *eretz*, to begin functioning properly. The earth itself provides all the raw materials necessary to begin the process of building the complex organisms we call life. Both of these creative forces, *eretz* (land) and *mayim* (water/chaos) are required to support this life, both of these in balance and in cooperation are what brings this about and the process, once started, continues in a path that results in reproduction and increasing in numbers.

Genesis 1:12

וַתּוֹצֵא הָאָרֶץ דֶּשֶׁא עֵשֶׂב מַזְרִיעַ זֶרַע לְמִינֵהוּ וְעֵץ עֹשֶׂה־פְּרִי אֲשֶׁר זַרְעוֹ־בוֹ לְמִינֵהוּ וַיַּרְא אֱלֹהִים כִּי־טוֹב:

The Land brought forth young green plants, sowing seed, for continuing his offspring. And trees produced fruit whose seed is in it for continuing its offspring. And the Powers saw the beauty.

In Verse 10 the Powers were defined, the 'dry land' and the 'sea.' In verse eleven these Powers are employed for bringing forth life on the land, green plants in particular. This verse is simply a parallel in which the action actually takes place. The Land produces/creates the 'young green plants,' the first life that takes its means for energy and reproduction from the sun itself.

The Land is not just there for the 'launch' either, so to speak, but is continually involved in the sowing. The plants have within themselves the 'seed' for continuing their offspring but it is the land that helps sow the seed. The wind, the water and gravity all conspire together to see that the seed is distributed far and wide so propagation can take place wherever climate and soil conditions are right for a particular plant.

Genesis 1:13

וַיְהִי־עֶרֶב וַיְהִי־בֹקֶר יוֹם שְׁלִישִׁי:

And there were Powers for watching chaos and Powers for illuminating order, a third work in chaos.

This third work in chaos is complete. The waters/chaos have been gathered/restricted, the dry land has appeared and with the establishment of the 'green plants,' the land has been 'filled.' Everything is functional and this 'triad' of 'days' is complete. Now the rest of the filling is about to take place.

Genesis 1:14

וַיֹּאמֶר אֱלֹהִים יְהִי מְאֹרֹת בִּרְקִיעַ הַשָּׁמַיִם לְהַבְדִּיל בֵּין הַיּוֹם וּבֵין הַלַּיְלָה וְהָיוּ לְאֹתֹת וּלְמוֹעֲדִים וּלְיָמִים וְשָׁנִים:

And he said, "Powers become a great light in the sheet of the skies for a dividing between the light and the darkness. And they are placed there for marking the way and for a witness and for working chaos and for years."

Ayn Soph now begins a series of commands to fill up or populate the things created in the previous verses. We begin with the sky. The powers, the *Elohim*, do not create the sun, they *become* the sun. *Elohim* is not just 'like' the sun, the *Elohim are* the sun. Again, we must rid ourselves of our dualism, the separation of the spiritual and the physical. Just as the sun is responsible for all life on earth, so is God. Earlier we said that the darkness in the creative process was substantive, it could be felt. The same is true of God's positive attributes. Light has substance just like the darkness. Scientists have theorized the solar sail for space travel based on this fact. The words used in our verse have substance, they are not simply vocalizations creating waves through space but they have substance, power, and creative energy. Words have physical reality, that is what makes language so powerful yet we have only scratched the surface of its power. Once spoken, words cannot be taken back; they have a power and life of their own. In the garden Y'shua simply said "I am he" and knocked professional soldiers off their feet. *Ayn Soph* spoke and the sun itself came into being. Men who understood a little of this power have changed history for good or evil, depending on the words. Even the words we are commentating on have changed the world. Let us be wise in their use.

The great light in our verse is plural in the Hebrew yet we have translated it in the singular because in this case we know we are talking about the sun (as verse sixteen will make clear) so the plural is for quality rather than quantity. Interestingly, however, it is followed up later in the verse by *them*, 'they are placed...' The *Elohim* throughout our translation are plural in quantity so it would be speculation to think there is a qualitative difference between them at this point. So we are left with the possibility that the sun is made up of more than one *Elohim* cooperating for effect or that there is a qualitative difference between *Elohim*, some are greater than others. This is not the only time we will see this. Later when Adam is created he was singular 'he created him' and then plural 'he created them.'

In verse seven and eight we stated that the *Elohim* are not only analogous to the continuum of order (*tam*) and chaos (*mot*) but that they are actually part of it. In our verse the *Elohim* of the *rakiah* become something tangible, they become the sun itself. This verse begins to show us the limits of the *rakiah*. It encompasses the earth to the depths of the sea and now it includes the sun. Perhaps it includes the known universe to which there may be a limit. The chaos being held back may be beyond the edge of the universe, the limits of the space which *Ayn Soph* made within itself for this creation. If the scientists who postulate multiple universes are correct, then the chaos outside of the universe would actually be the "matter" that exists between the universes.

The second half of the verse is an interesting construct pregnant with meaning. This part of the verse gives the reason for the creation of the 'Great Light.' Each word in the latter part of the verse begins with a 'lamed' (ל) meaning "for."[26] This emphasizes the continuity and the parallelism of the words. Parallelism is a poetic device in the Bible that states the same idea in a repetitive way with different words. In this conclusion of this verse there are two sets of parallels. Let's take the first group, 'marking the way' and 'working chaos.' First, remember our discussion of chaos thus far, including the idea that *mot* is death or 'chaos before the mark' and *dam* is blood or the 'door to chaos.' So here we have the idea that the 'Great Light' is placed there for the purpose of marking the way to a working in death or blood.

This could take us in several directions. Before the development of the world in our story, there was just *Ayn Soph*, eternal matter/energy distributed evenly everywhere. There was no real change. There is a question as to whether this was ever the case but for the sake of argument; let's just say it did at some point. When the development of the universe and our world began and matter was organized the tension between order and chaos began. The result of this is that change, the cycle of life, growth, decay and death, affected all things. In order for something to be created, matter has to be taken and reorganized from something else and that something else needs to cease to exist - die and be assimilated as matter or energy into the new entity. This is just as true for stars and planets as it is for the more obvious example of plants and animals feeding on other things to acquire energy for growth.

If we go back to the beginning, the first acts of creation required *Ayn Soph* to sacrifice some part of its self to create the *Elohim* and the world. John, in Revelation 13:8, says that Y'shua was "slain (sacrificed) on account of/as a result of the foundation of the world." Did it cause

---

[26] In the Masoretic text the last word שנים does not have the "lamed" however, other ancient texts such as the Dead Sea Scrolls does include the "lamed" as a prefix to this word.

pain for God to create the world? Was the organization of chaos painful; was some of the original 'blood' shed? The writer of Hebrews says we have a 'High Priest' that can sympathize with us. The pain all things, including us, experience as a part of life is built into the very fabric of reality. The sacrifices offered in the temple and the seasonal festivals point to this. The idea that God came in the form of a man in Christianity also supports this idea that sacrifice is the foundation of reality and without it, creation and growth is not possible. The object of life is not to eliminate pain and sacrifice but to put all things in balance, to embrace the discomforts, physical or mental/spiritual, necessary for growth and harmony.

Genesis 1:15

וְהָיוּ לִמְאוֹרֹת בִּרְקִיעַ הַשָּׁמַיִם לְהָאִיר עַל־הָאָרֶץ
וַיְהִי־כֵן:

**And they were set as lights in the sheet of the skies for the
lighting over the land and he stood firm.**

This verse repeats the idea that the *Elohim* are the lights in the *rakiah*
and it gives another purpose, they are there specifically for lighting the
land. Life on earth is not possible without the light and energy from
the sun, this verse simply states the obvious.

Genesis 1:16

וַיַּעַשׂ אֱלֹהִים אֶת־שְׁנֵי הַמְּאֹרֹת הַגְּדֹלִים אֶת־הַמָּאוֹר
הַגָּדֹל לְמֶמְשֶׁלֶת הַיּוֹם וְאֶת־הַמָּאוֹר הַקָּטֹן לְמֶמְשֶׁלֶת
הַלַּיְלָה וְאֵת הַכּוֹכָבִים:

And he made the powers, the two large lights and the stars, the large light for a ruler of the work in chaos and the small light for a ruler of the darkness.

It is interesting to note that the words 'sun' and 'moon' are not used until after the story of the flood, in the story of Avraham specifically. The reason for this could very well be the separation of the 'waters' diffused the light in the sky to the point where it was just light with no specific observable source. This would also explain why the rainbow was such a unique sign to Noah, it would have been impossible to observe in these atmospheric conditions.

That being the case, what about the stars? Certainly they would have been impossible to see through the haze. That is true, the stars could not be seen and you will notice we do not include it in our translation. The phrase 'and the stars' was added later, it is not in the versions of Genesis in the Dead Sea Scrolls. Even so, we can talk about them here because we know they were there, and have been there for millions of years even if the pre-flood world could not see them. In Isaiah 40:22 the prophet says that God "stretches out the heavens as a curtain." The black goat hair fibers of the tents of the Hebrews allowed pinholes of light through and appeared as the stars in the night. The ancients saw the stars as pinholes of light penetrating through the great tent above the earth, perhaps where the light of God Himself shone through. They are also permanent, they do not move in relation to

74

each other (at least not in one's lifetime) like the sun and moon. Men have always looked to the stars as things that told them something; the future, the past. In reality, they do tell us something of ancient history for when we look at them we are looking into the distant past. The writers of the scriptures personified them, telling us they fight[27], they have a moral quality[28] because they are the 'sons of God'[29] who praise God[30] and they are the spirits of God[31]. To the Ancient Hebrews the stars are more than just dots of light.

But let us return to what is actually in our verse, the 'great light' and now, the 'lesser light.' The sun and moon are representative of chaos and order. The sun is order, it rules over the chaos. The moon is like the original chaos, without the interjection of the light, it remains useless as a sign just as the chaos of creation would remain formless and useless without the interjection of the light. Historically, the night and the moon are associated with evil and chaos. But just as chaos can be brought into service, the moon, marking the months, shows that chaos can be brought into God's service. For the first light on the moon showing the new month is like the first appearance of light in the darkness.

---

[27] Judges 5:20
[28] Job 25:5
[29] Job 38:7
[30] Psalm 148:3
[31] Revelation 3:1

Genesis 1:17

וַיִּתֵּן אֹתָם אֱלֹהִים בִּרְקִיעַ הַשָּׁמָיִם לְהָאִיר עַל־הָאָרֶץ:

And he gave them Powers in the sheet of the skies for the light over the land.

This is an interesting verse. It seems like it is just repeating what had been said already and in some respects it is. The *Elohim are* the lights and they are placed in the sheet, the *rakiah*. Daniel 12:3 tells us that the lights are in the *rakiah*, including the stars which definitively define the *rakiah* as going from the surface of the ocean (water) to the edge of the universe which is the cavity of order created within *Ayn Soph* itself.

The real interesting thing in this verse is the verb *natan* which we have translated 'gave.' The question is, to whom or what did *Ayn Soph* 'give' the powers that are the lights in the *rakiah*? In order to figure this out, we should go through the process of elimination. Their purpose is for light over the land and they are part of the *rakiah* and they are the *Elohim* so they cannot be given to any of them, in reality anything in the *rakiah* would be exempted. What is left? The chaos outside the *rakiah*. It may seem odd to give the *Elohim* to the chaos but everything must be in balance and the inclusion of that which is outside (chaos) and that which is inside (order) maintains that balance.

76

Genesis 1:18

וְלִמְשֹׁל בַּיֹּום וּבַלַּיְלָה וּלֲהַבְדִּיל בֵּין הָאֹור וּבֵין הַחשֶׁךְ
וַיַּרְא אֱלֹהִים כִּי־טֹוב:

**And for ruling within a work in chaos and within the darkness
and for separating between the light and the chaotic darkness,
and the Powers saw the beauty.**

"For ruling within a work in chaos" shows the dynamic nature of creation as an ongoing process. In the *rakiah*, work continues to go on and it is the sun that is the source of all this activity and rules over it. It is not finished, it is an ongoing process. In the time of the Renaissance, the idea of God as a watchmaker who created the world and let it go on its own, is not too far from this idea. The world had been created to operate as a series of interacting parts and systems that work to establish and maintain balance and harmony. But it is not static like a watch but dynamic, constantly changing, developing and decaying. Over it all rules the sun, perhaps not just our own but countless stars ruling over countless solar systems providing the necessary energy for change and development.

Back on our world, it also is part of the regular changes that have to do with the previous verse's times and years. The seasons are circular and continuing because of these rulers, and creation remains dynamic through these cycles.

The second part of the verse shows us the parallelism of the whole story, pointing us back to the beginning when light and darkness were first separated and this separation was beautiful, it served a valuable function.

Genesis 1:19

וַיְהִי־עֶרֶב וַיְהִי־בֹקֶר יוֹם רְבִיעִי׃

And there were Powers for watching chaos and Powers for illuminating order, a fourth work in chaos.

This fourth work in chaos is complete.

Genesis 1:20

וַיֹּאמֶר אֱלֹהִים יִשְׁרְצוּ הַמַּיִם שֶׁרֶץ נֶפֶשׁ חַיָּה וְעוֹף יְעוֹפֵף
עַל־הָאָרֶץ עַל־פְּנֵי רְקִיעַ הַשָּׁמָיִם:

And he said, "The Powers swarm the waters, a swarm of nefesh chayah. And a flyer flies over the land, over the faces of the sheet of the skies.

This verse begins the filling of the sea and the land with something other than green plants. The verse begins with a command to *Elohim*, a new *Elohim* that is different from those of the previous verses related to the 'lights.' One could say that this *Elohim* is the "God of the sea/chaos" and this/these *Elohim* become the *nefesh chayah* of the water and the sky. This continues the idea that the 'stuff of God' infuses everything and that all is made out of the 'stuff of God.' The *Elohim* swarm over the water as the *nefesh chayah* and are understood as sea creatures. This makes the fish *Elohim*.

This idea necessitates an adjustment in our thinking in one of two ways. Either we change the way we think of 'God' to accommodate the idea that fish are 'God' or we change the way we think about fish. Do we elevate fish or do we bring God down? Neither. The *Elohim* in our translation thus far, have acted on creation and have been part of creation. They have active will and intelligence. To say that sentient beings partake of that is not so difficult. If the intelligence of God is that which we demonstrated with photons and manifests itself at the sub atomic level, it is not a stretch at all to say that sea creatures are of the same stuff.

The flyer is in the same mold yet there is something different. It is singular; in fact it is always singular (even in the next verse where we

79

translate it in the plural for clarity's sake). Perhaps this is because like a school of fish so many birds fly together in ways that make them seem like they have one mind, one consciousness. To see a flock of hundreds of birds move as one is a fascinating experience and challenges our common concepts of communication and consciousness as it relates to individual entities.

Ken Keyes related an amazing event that occurred to the Macaques monkeys in his book *The Hundredth Monkey*, which demonstrates the mysteries of the consciousness. "The Japanese monkey, Macaca fuscata, had been observed in the wild for a period of over 30 years. In 1952, on the island of Koshima, scientists were providing monkeys with sweet potatoes dropped in the sand. The monkeys liked the taste of the raw sweet potatoes, but they found the dirt unpleasant. An 18-month-old female named Imo found she could solve the problem by washing the potatoes in a nearby stream. She taught this trick to her mother. Her playmates also learned this new way and they taught their mothers too. This cultural innovation was gradually picked up by various monkeys before the eyes of the scientists. Between 1952 and 1958 all the young monkeys learned to wash the sandy sweet potatoes to make them more palatable. Only the adults who imitated their children learned this social improvement. Other adults kept eating the dirty sweet potatoes. Then something startling took place. In the autumn of 1958, a certain number of Koshima monkeys were washing sweet potatoes -- the exact number is not known. "Let us suppose that when the sun rose one morning there were 99 monkeys on Koshima Island who had learned to wash their sweet potatoes. Let's further suppose that later that morning, the hundredth monkey learned to wash potatoes. Then it happened! By that evening almost everyone in the tribe was washing sweet potatoes before eating them. The added energy of this hundredth monkey somehow created an ideological breakthrough! But notice. A most surprising thing observed by these scientists was that the habit of washing sweet potatoes then jumped over the sea – "Colonies of monkeys on other islands and the mainland troop of monkeys at Takasakiyama began washing their sweet potatoes. Thus, when a certain critical number achieves an awareness, this new awareness may be communicated from mind to mind. Although the exact number may vary, this Hundredth Monkey Phenomenon means that when only a limited number of people know of a new way, it may remain the conscious property of these people. But there is a point at which if only one more person tunes-in to a new awareness, a field is strengthened so that this awareness is picked up by almost everyone!

Genesis 1:21

וַיִּבְרָא אֱלֹהִים אֶת־הַתַּנִּינִם הַגְּדֹלִים וְאֵת כָּל־נֶפֶשׁ
הַחַיָּה הָרֹמֶשֶׂת אֲשֶׁר שָׁרְצוּ הַמַּיִם לְמִינֵהֶם וְאֵת
כָּל־עוֹף כָּנָף לְמִינֵהוּ וַיַּרְא אֱלֹהִים כִּי־טוֹב:

And the Powers filled the big tananim and all nefesh of the chayah the crawling one who swarms the waters to her bloodline and all flyers of the wing to her bloodline. And the Powers saw the beauty.

Here the fact that the *Elohim* are in the sea creatures are even more explicit. "The powers filled..." all the following. The first are the big *tananim*. *Tananim* is from *tanan* which is often translated as a snake, dragon or sea monster. It is probably something large and reptilian.

Now let's look at the phrase "*nefesh* of the *chayah*" We'll start with *nefesh*, a word we transliterated because no word in English really captures its meaning. *Nefesh* is a word composed of three Hebrew characters; the *nun* (ᔐ) a picture of a seed, the *peh* (ᔎ) a picture of the mouth and the *shin* (ᔎ) a picture of teeth. This word comes from a *peh/shin* root, which has the meaning of something that moves and has a mouth that eats. With the addition of the nun, we have a word that means "the seed of the mouth that eats." This is different than that of plants which generally don't move, at least not on their own, and don't have mouths.

It is more than this however. The mouth and movement are not just for sustenance. In contrast to plants that don't move, animals have some control over their location. They have that crucial item of self-determination; they can determine their own destiny. In addition, the mouth is something used for more than just chewing, it is used to communicate which adds the whole sociological aspect to the differentiation of plants and animals. Movement and communication are essential for cooperation, an important component of the higher animals. Finally, animals use oxygen, the breath, as opposed to plants that utilize carbon dioxide. This gives us the three fold component of all animals-the breath that energizes the being, the mind that gives it self determination and the body/flesh that encloses it all.

Before we leave the subject of *nefesh*, a recurring theme from here on out, we need to see not just the contrasts between plants and animals but their cooperation. The utilization of each other's waste comes to the fore. Science tells us that during the development of the planet primitive plants converted the toxic atmosphere to one that could sustain animal development. They cooperate in the exchange of gases, plants intake Carbon Dioxide and expel Oxygen while animals intake Oxygen and expel Carbon Dioxide. In addition, animals eat plants and plants utilize animal waste. This keeps everything in balance.

Finally, *nefesh* can also be translated as a sharp word. Everything was created as a result of words, so we can ask the question, does God have *nefesh*? Yes, Leviticus 26:30 specifically says so. Do all the things we have previously said about *nefesh* apply to God? God communicates, God 'moves.' God 'procreates' in the sense that the *Elohim* proceed from him and His word. Does God 'eat'? In this sense God does. The interdependence we have just described between animals (with *nefesh*) and plants describes the relationship God has with creation. God needs creation as much as creation needs God; they are interdependent, sustaining each other, cooperating to maintain balance. This only makes sense since we have already described how creation is made of the 'stuff of God.' God gives form and energy to creation, creation gives God substance and meaning.

Now let's look at the word *chayah* which is usually translated as 'life' from the more familiar root *chai* which many are familiar with. It is interesting that it is similar in meaning and pronunciation to the Chinese *chi*. In the Ancient Hebrew it is composed of a *chet* (ﬡ, a fence), a *yod* (ﬤﬞﬞﬞ, a hand/work) and a *hey* (ﬗ, behold). *Chayah* therefore had the meaning "behold the work of separation" which is the work of creation. *Chayah* therefore relates to consciousness, to be aware of one's environment, something that applies to animals. It is also related to the bloodline or the utilization of blood, to have the ability to utilize the breath (Oxygen). So *chayah* is to have blood and awareness.

Nefesh and *chayah* are singular and this expands on what we said in the previous verse. *Elohim* filled the *taninim* and the sea creatures and the birds and yet while *nefesh* is singular and *Elohim* is by definition plural, this again brings up the question of the *Elohim*, whether it is plural in quantity or quality. Do all living things share the same breath or *Elohim* that animates them? In a literal sense, they all operate by utilizing oxygen so they use the same breath. Job 12:10 states that in YHVH's hand is *nefesh* every *chayah* and the breath of all mankind. Perhaps all living things share one *Elohim* or the singular is simply to reiterate the interconnectedness of all things.

Genesis 1:22

וַיְבָ֧רֶךְ אֹתָ֛ם אֱלֹהִ֖ים לֵאמֹ֑ר פְּר֣וּ וּרְב֗וּ וּמִלְא֤וּ אֶת־הַמַּ֙יִם֙
בַּיַּמִּ֔ים וְהָע֖וֹף יִ֥רֶב בָּאָֽרֶץ׃

**And the Powers knelt to them to say bear fruit and become
great and complete, the waters in the seas and the flyers will
become great in the land.**

Now this seems like an odd verse. The powers knelt before this new creation, this is the first time this has happened. Kneeling shows submission or recognition of a superior power. This is the first time a sentient being was created that could replicate itself. The *Elohim* were created by *Ayn Soph* and infused all of creation but with the development of animals, fish and birds, beings that had will and the ability to impact their environment and could reproduce themselves.

Their mission, if we can call it that, was to fill the sea and the sky and by doing so they would complete them. Not only would they complete this part of creation but in doing so they would become great, they would experience a qualitative difference. What that is, we can only speculate.

Genesis 1:23

וַיְהִי־עֶרֶב וַיְהִי־בֹקֶר יוֹם חֲמִישִׁי׃

And there were Powers for watching chaos and Powers for illuminating order, a fifth work in chaos.

This fourth work in chaos is complete.

Genesis 1:24

וַיֹּאמֶר אֱלֹהִים תּוֹצֵא הָאָרֶץ נֶפֶשׁ חַיָּה לְמִינָהּ בְּהֵמָה
וָרֶמֶשׂ וְחַיְתוֹ־אֶרֶץ לְמִינָהּ וַיְהִי־כֵן:

**And he said, "Powers bring forth the nefesh chayah of the land
to her bloodline, a walker and a crawler and his chayah of land
belonging to her bloodline." And he stood firm.**

Based on what we have already discussed about *nefesh* and *chayah*,
this verse creates a lot of difficulties. We have this phrase "*nefesh
chayah* of the land" and the "*chayah* of land." Does the land/earth
have *nefesh* and *chayah*? *Nefesh* is a mouth that eats. I suppose it
would be reasonable to ask Korach[32] and the Egyptians[33] if that is true!
The land also replenishes itself with the waste and decomposition of
life. Does it communicate? The scriptures tell us that the earth
'groans' and 'bears witness.' It also procreates, in our verse it 'brings
forth.' Does it move? It has movement through space and within itself
in the form of earthquakes, mountain formation and continental shift.

What about *chayah*? *Chayah* was awareness and moving blood.
Awareness was handled under communication above. The earth is
made up of a large percentage of oxides and water, the same as our
bodies. Is this simply the writers using personification or some other
literary device? I think it's more than that. The people in the past were
close to the land, as opposed to people today who live in a mostly
artificial environment. People understood their relationship with the

---

[32] See Numbers 16:32

[33] See Exodus 15:12

land. From the American Indian to the Bedouin to the tribesmen of Africa or South America, they revered the natural world and sought to cooperate with it, they saw it as something living. We have come to look at the land as something to be used, a dead thing. If it is living, if it has 'consciousness,' then our attitude toward it and treatment of it, would have to change. It is easier for us to look at it as something wholly different from us than to see a kinship with it.

The fact that animals live, breath, communicate, and procreate means that the land has *nefesh chayah* because all sentient beings are part of it. *Nefesh chayah* and bloodline (usually translated 'kind') are singular because all beings created have one *nefesh*. The land was responsible for creating the *nefesh* from itself and spreading it out among all the animals. All sentient life is *echad* (one) because we all share the same *nefesh* just as the earth, though made up of many parts, is *echad*. The powers, the land and the *nefesh* are all paralleled in these verses showing that one emanates from the other and all are interrelated. With the land, created by the *Elohim*, producing *nefesh*, it is just producing according to her 'kind.' It is all made of the same 'stuff,' the stuff of God.

The denial of this 'oneness' is to be wicked according to the Scriptures. When the scriptures describe the destruction of the wicked, the analogy is often the grass being trodden down or destroyed[34]. Grass is non-sentient; it does not have *nefesh chayah*. Wickedness is the denial of one's *nefesh* which is also the denial of the 'oneness' of all things, the essential *echad* of the world. We have seen how this results in the destruction of the land by man simply using it as 'equipment' rather than something that is an integral part of himself. Sin is to separate, to work against harmony and cooperation, to deny *echad* and the result

---

[34] See Psalm 58:7 and Isaiah 5:24

of such an attitude and the resulting activity is annihilation. What we call 'civilization,' a consumer and wealth based society, is almost always based on the idea that the land and all sentient creatures (including man!) exist for our exploitation and all such societies have fallen in the past because of the disharmony they create. Presently, constituted nations are no different and *will* suffer the same fate.

Finally, let's look at the concept of 'bloodline,' ᴠᴡ (min) in Hebrew. The ᴠ is the water (or blood) and the ᴠ is seed that continues the life. Hence, the bloodline is the blood that continues. We know that this is actually the DNA that carried the 'type' or characteristics to the next generation and makes it a 'line.' "Her bloodline" refers to the land and this is why the blood is to be returned to the earth[35]. It was formed from the land and it belongs to the land so it must return to the land when it is no longer being used within the body. All living things that have blood belong to the bloodline of the land.

---

[35] Deuteronomy 15:23

Genesis 1:25

וַיַּעַשׂ אֱלֹהִים אֶת־חַיַּת הָאָרֶץ לְמִינָהּ וְאֶת־הַבְּהֵמָה לְמִינָהּ וְאֵת כָּל־רֶמֶשׂ הָאֲדָמָה לְמִינֵהוּ וַיַּרְא אֱלֹהִים כִּי־טוֹב:

And the Powers aligned the chayah of the land to her bloodline and the walker to her bloodline and all the crawler of the ground to his bloodline. And the Powers saw the beauty.

In the previous verse, the 'oneness' of all things was emphasized. In this verse, everything is separated into its own bloodline. But this is not to negate what went on before, even though there are different bloodlines, all is still interrelated and *echad* and coming from the land.

Genesis 1:26

וַיֹּאמֶר אֱלֹהִים נַעֲשֶׂה אָדָם בְּצַלְמֵנוּ כִּדְמוּתֵנוּ וְיִרְדּוּ
בִדְגַת הַיָּם וּבְעוֹף הַשָּׁמַיִם וּבַבְּהֵמָה וּבְכָל־הָאָרֶץ
וּבְכָל־הָרֶמֶשׂ הָרֹמֵשׂ עַל־הָאָרֶץ:

And the Powers said, "We will make an adam in our shadow, like our origin. And they journeyed among the swimmers of the sea and among the flyers of the skies and among the walkers and among all the land and among all the crawlers over the land."

This verse begins a whole new set of ideas; the parallels of the previous six days are now over. Verse four was described as the 'E=mc2' verse of the created order, this verse parallels that in that this is the crucial verse describing the purpose and nature of man. It is the powers, the *Elohim*, who are the creative forces in this verse. The 'we' refers to all of them. Man is made of the *Elohim*, divided into the sky and the land. The land contributes the dust, the physical form. The sky contributes the *ruach*, the wind, the breath. The animals were made of one or the other; they were created by the *Elohim* that is the land or the *Elohim* that is the sky. Man was created by both and shares characteristics of both. That makes man, as Y'shua said when quoting the psalms, *Elohim*[36].

'An *adam*' is a recognition that this is not a proper name but refers to what was created. Its name comes from the Hebrew word for blood, *dam*, which as we have pointed out previously, in the ancient pictographs means 'the door to chaos.' The aleph, which precedes the

---

[36] John 10:34

91

word *dam*, gives the meaning of head or strong. So the *adam* is literally 'the strong door to chaos.' This concerns what comes next. 'Our shadow....our origin' refers to the fact that the *adam* is made as *Elohim* was made. A shadow is a representation of the original and it is also connected to, and inseparable from, that original. We were created to be a reflection of the divine nature of the universe, of *Elohim* as emanated from *Ayn Soph*. We reflect the character, and even movements of the divine, just as a shadow does for that which creates it. It is when we learn we are a self, when we develop 'ego,' that the shadow breaks from the original, we lose our connection to the divine and the universe, and the *shalom* that that connection brings. Everything was created *echad*, it is by consciously fostering the illusion of separation that we lose our connection with the *Elohim*.

That was the shadow; we are also made like *Elohim*'s origin. The origin of *Elohim* was in the primordial chaos. This is why we chose to translate *damut* as origin. *Dam*-blood and *damam*-silent are all related words and concepts. In verse four, the *Elohim* for 'watching chaos' are contrasted with the active *Elohim* 'illuminating order.' Man is formed in the chaos/silence (passive)/blood. The *adam* starts in the same place as everything else, in chaos. The *adam*, however, is different from the rest of creation. The animals were made and they develop according to a prescribed pattern, they act according to their instincts. They developed out of an order that already existed, the sky/water or the land. They are therefore limited in their latitude for growth and development. They are like a clay pot that has already been formed and simply needs paint and glaze to finish. The options for the use of the pot are limited by the shape that already exists. The *adam* is different. It is made from the chaos, it starts where *Elohim* did and because of that, the possibilities are limitless. The *adam* is a lump of clay with no shape or form. It can be made into anything, but at its beginning it is chaotic, useless. The limits of man's becoming do not exist. The catch is that the chaos has to be worked, energy needs to be applied.

We have translated *radan* as 'journey.' *Radan* means to walk with the head down, deliberately, carefully, in humility. The walking or treading on something is where the idea of ruling comes in, but we have concentrated on the walking. The ancient Hebrew pictographs give a meaning like 'the primary door to perpetuity.' Our journey is one to the eternal. It is a journey that begins in chaos and every step brings more order. Y'shua, for example, followed this pattern as he "grew in wisdom and stature," he went from chaos to order, from immaturity to maturity. As we take steps along the journey we have the same choice the *adam* did, the choice between wisdom and knowledge. At some point early in life we choose, or are taught, to take one path or the other. In the western world, we choose knowledge. It is a fork in the road and we start on the path of knowledge. To change this course, we must return to the fork and begin on the other path. Y'shua said we must become as little children, we must go back to where we chose wrongly and learn the path of wisdom.

As we begin our journey from chaos to order, we do so among the rest of creation. We have described things in the Hebrew fashion, according to function. Hence swimming and flying things rather than birds or fish. We walk among this order of which we are a part, yet different. We are less ordered, yet our potential is limitless. We partake of each segment of the creation, yet we are greater than the sum of its parts. We learn from it, we learn about the divine from it. Paul tells us in Romans one that all of creation tells us about the essential nature of God, and by extension, ourselves. In a rudimentary fashion, we learn from nature and learn to use it. We learn dam building from beavers, tunnels from moles, flying from birds. We harness electricity from lightning, we heat and cook with fire. But it is all more than that. The Bible, particularly as one looks at the Paleo-Hebrew pictographs, is replete with animal and natural imagery. In Genesis 1:2 the *ruach* of *Elohim* is brooding over the waters, much like a mother bird over her chicks. The world around us tells us about ourselves and we connect with the divine through it. In the Bible as well as in other religious traditions around the world, meditation was done most effectively in the wilderness. To turn inward and upward we must get out of the artificial environment man creates through his ego and out into the untouched world so we can see and hear things as they really are. This is one of the reasons why man will construct artificial environments, such as parks, to reflect a natural space within cities. Our ego worries because it is concerned with the preservation of the illusion of self. As we are surrounded with people who are just as worried, it is difficult to escape the bondage that results. Y'shua said we are to look at the birds of the air, who only act as they are created to, they do not worry, and they have no image to protect. If we choose the right path, the path of wisdom, of life, of *echad*, we too will become as they are. Our chaos will be molded as Y'shua's was, into the most functional implement for our place within the order of the universe. We will connect with *Ayn Soph* and that connection will properly order us as it did the *Elohim* during the days of creation.

Genesis 1:27

וַיִּבְרָא אֱלֹהִים אֶת־הָאָדָם בְּצַלְמוֹ בְּצֶלֶם אֱלֹהִים בָּרָא
אֹתוֹ זָכָר וּנְקֵבָה בָּרָא אֹתָם:

And he commanded and the Powers filled the man with his shadow, with the shadow of the Powers he filled him, mind and womb he filled them.

Now, we are about to finish the creation to our present era with the actual development of man. The *Elohim* are the ones that do the work in this verse, filling *adam* with 'his' shadow. Who is 'he'? It can be none other than *Ayn Soph*, something unique in the world of sentient beings. The shadow of *Ayn Soph* includes that spark that began it all; it is the infinite within us, a communion not with all the intermediaries of creation like the land or *Elohim* but with the primal force. That gives man a potential far greater than any animal, for good or evil.

But this is not the whole story because we are also filled with the shadow of the powers by *Ayn Soph*. We saw that in the last verse. This is the first time in a number of verses that *Ayn Soph* has been directly involved in creation, another unique happening. Being filled with the shadow of the *Elohim* encompasses all of the created order including our earlier continuum from *tam* to *mot*. Man is not simply the last thing created but includes all that went before.

Continuing with this thread, we can now look at the 'mind' and the 'womb.' The mind and womb could represent the two extremes of the spectrum of the created order, as was mentioned above. But there is more. These two aspects of man garner special mention because of their crucial nature in our purpose. These two things are filled, but with what? The mind is something that looks back, it remembers the past, one's origins. The womb is taking this knowledge to the next generation, figuratively and literally. The feasts mirror this idea, for time in Hebrew is always connected with that which was before and that which comes after. The feasts celebrate historical events but also point to the future. Future events flow from the present and the past and part of our 'mission' is to connect things, to learn and develop so we can more effectively fulfill our purpose.

This verse ends with the creation of 'man' and then describes him as 'them.' There are two possibilities here. The first is that it refers to the totality of mankind embodied in the *adam*, coded in his DNA. Therefore, we all received the command, we all experience what the *adam* did, we all have his potential. The other possibility is that instead of one individual, the *adam* is a community of beings, male and female. The usual translation of the story would support the latter but our translation could support the former.

Genesis 1:28

וַיְבָרֶךְ אֹתָם אֱלֹהִים וַיֹּאמֶר לָהֶם אֱלֹהִים פְּרוּ וּרְבוּ
וּמִלְאוּ אֶת־הָאָרֶץ וְכִבְשֻׁהָ וּרְדוּ בִּדְגַת הַיָּם וּבְעוֹף
הַשָּׁמַיִם וּבְכָל־חַיָּה הָרֹמֶשֶׂת עַל־הָאָרֶץ:

**The Powers knelt to them and the Powers said to them, "Bear
fruit and become great, and complete the land and rule her,
and journey among the swimmers of the sea and among the
fliers of the skies and among all the chayah crawling on the
land."**

The powers again kneel before these new creations, recognizing the
unique nature of this aspect of creation. It is even more than that
however. There is a big difference between the fish and birds and the
adam. The *Elohim* were separated in past verses, becoming or creating
various parts of the natural order. This separation in some sense
'diluted' them, making them less than the whole. Adam was made
from their totality, the powers, the sky and the land; he was the sum
total of their parts and even more because he also has the shadow of
Ayn Soph. It is almost like the science fiction dream of creating a
computer or machine that does a specific job better than we do with
the addition of artificial intelligence. In this case the job was to work
cooperatively with the *Elohim*, becoming one with them in the work of
filling the earth and completing creation.

The picture here is one of a parent kneeling down to look in the child's
eyes, communicating the hope that the child will grow up and take
his/her place, continuing and improving upon the work started by the
parent. When he is commanded to 'bear fruit,' he is to remove the
husk from the kernel of his being (the seed). The powers created a

97

being that was the best of them all in combination, yet had the potential for growth. It is our growth in righteousness and intimacy with our creator that accomplishes the goal for filling the earth.

The phrase 'bear fruit' and 'become great' refer to two aspects of man. The first is generally accepted as procreation, the population of the earth, a command given to other aspects of creation. The second refers the ability to grow, to become much more than what he was originally created. It is the development of an individual 'spiritually' to enable him/her to have the wisdom necessary to accomplish the mission. An animal is an animal and all of its species are basically the same. People, on the other hand, can be very different, behave differently, and develop different aspects of character and behavior going far beyond basic instinct.

The word translated 'to complete' is *mahal* which comes from the root *mahl* which means to reduce. Our job is to complete the creation by reducing chaos and imbalance and to reduce the emptiness by 'filling.' We are to utilize our creative faculties to complete the creative process. Where does this wisdom come from? It comes from creation itself. We are to journey among all the creatures of the world, learning from them and about them, ascertaining how we can best bring about balance and harmony in the world. It is by becoming part of the natural order that we can understand it and find our proper place within it, while becoming aware of anything that creates disharmony. By doing so, we become the caretakers (rulers) of creation.

It is important to understand that there is a progression between completing and ruling. We must do the former in order to do the latter. We learn the how of completion from the journey we take. Creation is waiting and groaning[37] because we have never done this.

---

[37] Romans 8:22

We have studied it, we have exploited it, we have polluted it, we have tried to fix it but we have never completed it, we have never valued it, never seen it as something beautiful in and of itself. Every major civilization that has arisen in history has sought to impose artificial constrains on the world and conquer those who did not share their worldview. As a result, it is wallowing in its uncompleted, chaotic state.

This raises several questions. Can we still complete our purpose? Are we the redeemers of the earth and if so, have we failed? I would say yes to both. The wealth and consumer driven society that we call 'progress' and 'civilization' has spread like a cancer all over the world and even societies that don't yet participate have the desire to do so. To reverse this trend, the mentality of progress as defined by material things in which waste of resources for no purpose but to satisfy our appetites that has been in existence since the first city was built, is too entrenched in the mentality of man to be dislodged.

There is another question that arises from this failure of ours. Are we, or at least what we have become, the intention of *Ayn Soph*? Did the *Elohim* make something that was a little 'unexpected' that did not exactly turn out as intended? The later story of the flood gives us a clue that instead of the crowning achievement of creation we are more like Frankenstein's monster! Is the judgment visited on the earth, the flood being the latest example, an attempt to rid the creation of our infestation, like so many cockroaches? It is something to think about. There is a saying that the nail that sticks up is the one that gets hit. We were created to be a part of the world, not over and above it, seeing ourselves as separate. As we separate ourselves from the created order instead of fitting into the place that maintains balance, we stick up and out of place. That makes us a target and the more we distance ourselves from the created order and surround ourselves with an artificial environment, the larger a target we become in the reaction of the world to reestablish order.

Genesis 1:29

וַיֹּאמֶר אֱלֹהִים הִנֵּה נָתַתִּי לָכֶם אֶת־כָּל־עֵשֶׂב זֹרֵעַ זֶרַע
אֲשֶׁר עַל־פְּנֵי כָל־הָאָרֶץ וְאֶת־כָּל־הָעֵץ אֲשֶׁר־בּוֹ פְרִי־עֵץ
זֹרֵעַ זָרַע לָכֶם יִהְיֶה לְאָכְלָה:

And the Powers said, "Look, I gave to you(plural) the whole green plant, a seeding of seed which is over the face of all the land and the whole of the tree which in him a fruit tree a seeding a seed, for you(plural). He will mediate for food."

At the beginning of the food chain are plants. They are responsible for life on earth, converting the energy of the sun and the minerals of the soil into food energy that can be assimilated by animals. They also produce the air we breathe. We could say that plants were placed here for our sustenance, that that is their purpose.

A closer look at the verse reveals a parallel between 'I give you' and 'he will mediate for food.' The *Elohim* are talking and *adam* is being referred to so who is 'he'? The only one left is *Ayn Soph*. Apparently it is some quality of *Ayn Soph*, the basic energy force of the universe that infuses plants with their life giving qualities. This is apart from the basic energy supplied by *Ayn Soph* to all things. The plants of *Ayn Soph* are the mediators by which the *Elohim* of the sky/sun and the *Elohim* of the land transfer energy to animals and to us.

There are several different kind of plants listed in this verse. 'Green plant' and 'tree' are singular. Obviously they include, numerically, more than one organism but they are all *echad*, there is only one great organism composed of many individual parts. Within the tree, for example, is a fruit tree bearing seeds and fruit that is for food. A 'seeding of seed' refers to plants that are grown by the intervention of man. The *adam* sowed and reaped in the garden, cultivated fruit trees, etc. This is why the curse in a later verse had such meaning. The ground that he had previously sown would not easily give up its fruit as it had before. The cooperation between the sky, the land and man was broken, now the land needs to be 'coerced' to yield her bounty.

Genesis 1:30

וּלְכָל־חַיַּת הָאָרֶץ וּלְכָל־עוֹף הַשָּׁמַיִם וּלְכֹל רוֹמֵשׂ
עַל־הָאָרֶץ אֲשֶׁר־בֹּו נֶפֶשׁ חַיָּה אֶת־כָּל־יֶרֶק עֵשֶׂב לְאָכְלָה
וַיְהִי־כֵן׃

**"And all green plants are for all the life of the land and for all
the flyers of the skies and for all the crawlers over the land
which is in him nefesh chayah." And he stood firm.**

The green plants are not just for the *adam*, but for all the creatures
that were created 'in him.' This *nefesh chayah* refers, not just too all
the creatures previously named, but to the *Elohim* who share this
nefesh chayah. This verse, just before everything wraps up, restates
what has been emphasized all along, everything is *echad*, from the
powers to the *rakiah*, to the sky and land and everything in it,
including us.

Genesis 1:31

וַיַּרְא אֱלֹהִים אֶת־כָּל־אֲשֶׁר עָשָׂה וְהִנֵּה־טוֹב מְאֹד
וַיְהִי־עֶרֶב וַיְהִי־בֹקֶר יוֹם הַשִּׁשִּׁי:

And the Powers saw all that he became and look, an all encompassing beauty. And there were Powers for watching chaos and Powers for illuminating order, the sixth work in chaos.

The *Elohim* now stands back and looks at what he had become, like a woman who has done herself up to go out may admire herself in a mirror. *Ayn Soph* is the raw material of creation, the *Elohim* are what that raw material is fashioned into. Not only is it 'beautiful' as the individual parts were, it is an "all encompassing beauty," all the parts are now combined together into one great functioning whole. Not only is it complete in the sense that all the parts are there, but it is developing in a way that makes it much greater than the sum of its parts. There was filling and multiplying and man was developing. All this made creation much more than a machine, but a whole, dynamic living, growing entity.

There is another difference in the wording of this verse that is different from the previous verses, and that is the letter *hey* (𐤀), which is prefixed to the word meaning sixth to show that this day is different. A *hey* is a picture of a man who is beholding something. The change could reflect the fact that man was here to see the conclusion of this day or that we are currently beholding the sixth day, and that this work in chaos is not yet complete.

104

Genesis 2:1

וַיְכֻלּוּ הַשָּׁמַיִם וְהָאָרֶץ וְכָל־צְבָאָם:

And they were completed, the sky and the land and all their army.

The *Elohim* that make up all of creation are now finished, completed, they no longer have a creative function. In this position, they now become susceptible to the second law of thermodynamics, the law that says that all systems decay over time. The *Elohim* know this and it could very well be that the creation of man was the attempt to stop this slide into chaos, to have a renewable source of creative intelligence and energy that would keep the earth from descending into chaos. As a later verse will say, man is to guard and maintain the garden, he is to keep the chaos out, or at least at bay. Needless to say, we have failed miserably in our duty and the creation that reached its peak of creative power and energy in this verse has continued to deteriorate since then. We have allowed the earth to be cursed and it will continue to slide deeper and deeper into chaos.

The word *tzeva* is usually translated as host, but literally meaning an army. The armies in this case are the *Elohim* and the *Elohim* correspond to the individual aspects of creation. This verse forms a complete action by pointing back to the beginning with the reference to the *Elohim*, the sky and the land. This verse also points to the oneness (*echad*) of all things. The 'they' are the *Elohim*, the sky and the land. They are the *Elohim* that became them, and they are all one 'host' or 'army.' The *tzeva,* at the conclusion, therefore parallels and represents all of creation, the host of *Elohim* that make up all things.

Genesis 2:2

וַיְכַל אֱלֹהִים בַּיּוֹם הַשְּׁבִיעִי מְלַאכְתּוֹ אֲשֶׁר עָשָׂה וַיִּשְׁבֹּת
בַּיּוֹם הַשְּׁבִיעִי מִכָּל־מְלַאכְתּוֹ אֲשֶׁר עָשָׂה:

And he completed the Powers in the seventh work of chaos, his instructions which he filled and he stopped in the seventh work of chaos, from all his instructions which he filled.

The 'he' in this verse is *Ayn Soph,* and the *Elohim* (Powers) and instructions are paralleled. This refers back to our discussion of 'intelligence' and what it means for creation to be made of the 'stuff of God.' The instructions were for the continual unfolding of things as they were created. He filled the *Elohim*/instructions and then stopped, nothing else needed to be done, the *Elohim* were now on 'autopilot.' There was no need for *Ayn Soph* to do any more 'work.' It was now up to *Elohim* to embody and fulfill the instructions, and for man to cooperate with this work.

The function of man, the only active force left, and the Powers (*Elohim*) as a passive entity, is to bring about more order and to fill up the creation. This takes work, although at this stage everything is in balance, so the work required would be minimal. The *Shabbat* is not a picture of rest in the sense of doing nothing but the rest that results when things are in harmony and 'work' is easy. When things are out of balance, it requires more work to restore balance. How much depends on how out of balance things are. For example, when the *adam* was placed in the garden things came easily. Everything was in order and all cooperated to bring about optimal results. The *adam* was in harmony with all things. He planted and gathered without difficulty, for everything grew in its place and was functional. After 'the fall,' things were in disorder, chaos became the rule. Weeds grew with the feed plants; the soil did not give up its nutrients as easily. That was only the beginning.

Everything is perfectly in balance at this point. *Ayn Soph* has worked to establish an order from the chaos and has everything functional as it should be. When *Ayn Soph* stopped working, the *adam* was there as one created in his shadow, with his creative abilities charged with the task of maintaining order and harmony. To keep balance is easy. If you watch a circus performer doing an act that requires balance, they can find a place and stand still with little effort. That was the way things were. But it takes some work and focus to stay in balance. The minute that work ceases, balance is lost. For our circus performer, he begins wild gyrations that result in a tremendous expense of effort to readjust one way and then another until either he falls off or restores balance. At some point the *adam* ceased working, taking the created order for granted and no longer understanding his crucial place as its partner and allowed more and more chaos in, upsetting the balance. After 'the fall,' things were in disorder, chaos became the rule. Weeds grew with the feed plants, the soil did not give up its nutrients as easily. This has been compounded over the millennia. Right now things are way out of balance and it would require a major readjustment to restore balance. That readjustment can be at our instigation, or as the result of nature's work, which is generally a catastrophic readjustment.

This was the message of Noah; this was the message of Y'shua. Both sought to bring comfort and hope to those feeling helpless under the burden imposed by years of either neglect or the active introduction of chaos. There was/is still time, but it wasn't forever. The *Elohim* of creation will slowly decay (2nd Law of Thermodynamics) if no additional energy is injected. The natural order is to go from creation to destruction and recreation. The length of that process is up to us.

Throughout our story so far, *Ayn Soph* has injected energy and creative power into the universe that reversed the normal process of decay. *Ayn Soph* has now stopped. The *Elohim*, as active participants in this process have now been relegated to a passive role and they know what the eventual result of that will be. We are the wild card. We were created by the *Elohim* with their totality, in a sense greater than all of them, and we were created in the Shadow of *Ayn Soph*, with its creative power and energy. It could very well be that we are to be the saviors of the world, to keep the *Elohim* from destruction by continuing to help them become ordered and filled. This may sound absolutely fantastic to most, but we believe we have not even begun to scratch the surface of our potential. And we are not talking about technology here, that has just hastened our descent into chaos. It was the teaching of Y'shua and the prophets that point the way. Israel was to live this kind of *Shabbat* existence in the land and they blew it and destruction overtook them. Every individual, every society, every generation has the ability and responsibility to bring about balance and harmony. The fall of the *adam* was the first step into the descent into chaos, but every one of us has the power of *Ayn Soph* within us to reverse that step, to restore things. Creation is counting on us.

Genesis 2:3

וַיְבָרֶךְ אֱלֹהִים אֶת־יוֹם הַשְּׁבִיעִי וַיְקַדֵּשׁ אֹתוֹ כִּי בוֹ שָׁבַת
מִכָּל־מְלַאכְתּוֹ אֲשֶׁר־בָּרָא אֱלֹהִים לַעֲשׂוֹת:

**And the Powers knelt on the seventh work in chaos and
He(Powers) assigned him(Shabbat) because in him He(Ayn Soph)
stopped from all his instructions which he filled the Powers
for function.**

In this verse the Powers kneel again, this time before *Ayn Soph*. Note that we have a seventh work in Chaos. There was work being done but not of the same kind that was done in the previous verses. Instead of 'sanctifies' or some other such translation of *kadosh* we have chosen 'assigned.' The word *kadosh* means to set aside or assign something a specific purpose. In this case the *shabbat* is assigned the function of marking the time when the powers had been filled with their instructions and *Ayn Soph* stopped. Creation had been completed as far as the creative energy of *Ayn Soph* was concerned; it was now a functional unity where each specific component has a role that contributes to the well being and harmony of the whole. The *Elohim* are 'programmed' this way, to maintain their position and make their contribution. We are not. We seem to think we can move outside our function, differentiate ourselves from creation, do things better than the original. This was Korach's mistake in Exodus. He came to Moshe and said that all God's people were holy (*kadosh*). That is true, each one of God's people are assigned a specific function within the whole. Korach's mistake was his assumption that those functions were the same, or were interchangeable. They are not. We may think we can improve on nature. For example, we straighten rivers and harness them behind levies and dams. Then we complain when the surrounding floodplain needs chemical fertilizers to grow food, or why the deposits pollute our waterways, or the failure of the dams lead to loss of life, or the fish don't spawn upstream anymore. The same is true of so many of the medicines we think we need (50% of Americans take at least one prescription drug, 25% take two or more), many of which we need as a result of our poisoned environment. Nature has so many cures, yet the almighty dollar says we must make synthetics that can be patented and sold. We believe that our technology and innovation over the past hundred years has made our lives better and healthier. In fact, we are poisoning ourselves with our progress. Diseases that were practically unknown one hundred years ago have come to the forefront because of our tampering with our food and environment. Let me give you some examples. In 1900 cancer was responsible for three percent of the deaths in the U.S., now it is 20%. Diabetes affected one tenth of one percent, now it is 20%. Fifty years ago, breast cancer affected one in twenty women, now it is one in three. Heart attacks as a result of coronary artery disease were virtually unknown in the early 1900s. Autism makes if first appearance in 1931. In just the 23 years between 1973 and 1996 prostate cancer increased 126%, childhood leukemia 17%, childhood brain cancer 26%, breast cancer 25% and testicular cancer 41%. Our food is contaminated with pesticides, antibiotics, heavy metals and a host of other chemicals. Even mothers breast milk contains traces of a component of rocket fuel[38]. Our air and water are polluted. Our homes are made of things known to be unhealthy. Better living through synthetics? I don't think so. If we would let each part of nature have its role, and learn to live comfortably in our place within it, life would be much simpler and healthier.

---

[38] The Hundred Year Lie, Randall Fitzgerald. Dutton books, 2006

We can wonder at this point, what are the instructions, exactly? What are instructions? Instructions are a messenger that tells another what to do. The instructions that come with a child's bicycle are the message given by the manufacturer as to how to assemble it. The instructions in this case are the words from *Ayn Soph* that formed the *Elohim* into the various parts of creation and guide them in their development, in the accomplishing of their work. These messages could be construed as the laws that govern the universe and how its parts come together, and eventually, apart. Atomic and molecular structures, DNA and the genetic code are all instructions that keep this world functioning and developing, separating and filling. This day is a memorial to the wisdom and intelligence of *Ayn Soph* and to the wonderful capacity of the instruction given so long ago to develop and maintain this wonderful universe.

Genesis 2:4

אֵלֶּה תוֹלְדוֹת הַשָּׁמַיִם וְהָאָרֶץ בְּהִבָּרְאָם בְּיוֹם עֲשׂוֹת
יְהוָה אֱלֹהִים אֶרֶץ וְשָׁמָיִם:

**These are offspring of the skies and land in their being made
full, in a work of chaos YHVH the Powers made land and
skies.**

This is the first verse since chapter one verse one that doesn't start
with the letter *vav*, meaning and, so we have a new thought
introduced here. It would seem that there is a second creation story
beginning here, perhaps another tradition or even a more specific
account of what went before. It also introduces YHVH, one of the
Elohim, a unique creative participant. The whole thing begins with the
development of the sky and the land again. But the next verse only
takes us back to day three, not at the beginning. Let's consider one
more possibility.

There could be a type of cataclysm between what was created
previously and what is next. The plants were created yet according to
the next verse, there are no plants. How could this be? Perhaps a
massive volcanic eruption spewed ash and gasses into the atmosphere
causing a rapid cooling that killed most of the plants, people and
animals of the previous creation. We know this has happened, even
within recorded history, on a smaller scale. In this case a few survived,
the *adam* being one, because he was prepared. The particulate matter
eventually fell out and the gases created a greenhouse effect which
evaporated the water and placed it in the heavens waiting for the
flood. This is only speculation, but it could explain some of what

happens next and the differences between the previous account and this one. Keep all this in mind as we go on.

Genesis 2:5

וְכֹל שִׂיחַ הַשָּׂדֶה טֶרֶם יִהְיֶה בָאָרֶץ וְכָל־עֵשֶׂב הַשָּׂדֶה
טֶרֶם יִצְמָח כִּי לֹא הִמְטִיר יְהוָה אֱלֹהִים עַל־הָאָרֶץ וְאָדָם
אַיִן לַעֲבֹד אֶת־הָאֲדָמָה:

**And all plant life of the field, that existed before in the land
and all plants of the field before they will grow because
YHVH the Powers had not caused rain over the land and
without an adam for serving the ground.**

The next several verses describe what the world was like before the new story commences. There was one sea out of which the rivers in the following verses come. The 'field' refers to a level land where there were few, if any, mountains. There was no rain which is a result of certain weather systems. If there was some kind of canopy surrounding the earth, it would have kept temperatures reasonably constant everywhere, and the temperature differentials and the geography of the world, perhaps even the lack of great bodies of water, would have mitigated against the formation of weather fronts that produce rain.

"Plant life....that existed before.." could refer to the cataclysm postulated in the previous verse or it could be that they had not had time to spread out beyond their original places of creation, near the next verse's water sources. One thing that is clear is that both man and YHVH the powers cooperate in spreading plant growth over the face of the earth.

Finally, we have to bring up the question of the chronology of the previous story and this one. In order for the story about the plants, and later, animals, to be created after man, there may be at least three possibilities. First, the chronology of the previous verses needs to be ignored. Chapter one was a poetic chronology, not a literal one. This would ignore the wonderful science that can be brought to bear supporting such a chronology. The question then becomes, what was the author's purpose in ordering it as he did? The second possibility is that there was a cataclysm and recreation before this story began. Finally, we can put forward one more theory. Perhaps what follows is a story about a particular place within creation, the garden, and it no longer is referring to the world as a whole. This would mean that plants, animals and man would exist elsewhere in the world, but the particular area discussed in the following two chapters of Genesis is unique. We will go on and see what makes the most sense.

Genesis 2:6

וְאֵד יַעֲלֶה מִן־הָאָרֶץ וְהִשְׁקָה אֶת־כָּל־פְּנֵי־הָאֲדָמָה:

And mist came up from the land and gave drink to all the faces of the ground.

This verse gives us an idea of how the plants were growing without rain. The word we translate 'mist' is like a smoke or a fog. We can speculate about a heavy dew or even the possibility that geysers provided the mist that watered areas where the plants grew. The plants would be limited to the immediate areas surrounding these sources, which is a connection to the 'plant life' of the previous verse, which is a Hebrew word that means the wall of plants that surrounds a pond.

The ground (*adamah*), that is watered, sets up what comes next. It refers to the ground out of which the *adam* is formed. The next verse says that the *adam* was formed much as a potter forms a clay pot. In addition to the clay/ground the potter also needs water, which is provided in this verse. The land is the land around the sea somewhere outside the 'garden' where the *adam* is formed and then brought to the garden.

Genesis 2:7

וַיִּיצֶר יְהוָה אֱלֹהִים אֶת־הָאָדָם עָפָר מִן־הָאֲדָמָה וַיִּפַּח
בְּאַפָּיו נִשְׁמַת חַיִּים וַיְהִי הָאָדָם לְנֶפֶשׁ חַיָּה:

**And YHVH the Powers pressed out the adam of the multitude
from Ha'adamah. And he blew into his nostrils a nesh'mat
chayim and the adam existed for the nefesh chayah.**

This is a crucial verse describing the essential nature of man, so we will
take it phrase by phrase. It is time to deal with the issue of what or
who is YHVH the powers. The powers (*Elohim*) are the totality of
creation. It is, in a sense, all matter. YHVH is one of the *Elohim*, the
one that supplies the kinetic energy, the active force, the 'first and
continuing cause,' that brings the order of creation about. It is, at its
root, impersonal. Therefore we have to redefine some terms,
particularly relational ones. 'Knowing YHVH' is being in harmony with
the creative force in its totality. As we read the biblical text and see
people relating to or talking to YHVH, it is an attempt to use a
common point of reference and the limits of common language and
terms to describe a transcendent experience. It is similar to the
relation of a dream. When we see the Scriptures having two or more
YHVH's in a text doing different and sometimes opposite functions[39]
we attempt to try to wrap our Greek minds around it and make sense
of it by applying the rules of logic. However, dreams do not follow
logical patterns and have their own rules of interpretation. The key to
understanding YHVH is to first find the proper way to understand the

---

[39] An example of this can be found in Exodus 12:23 where YHVH is identified
as the one who will kill the firstborn, the destroyer, but is also the one who
prevents the destroyer from killing the firstborn in the house where the blood
is found on the doorframe.

way the experience has been related by the person who had it and then enter into that experience so one can understand the common points of reference.

Idolatry is simply a result of misinterpreting or failing to embrace the transcendent experience. Those who have not had an experience with the creative force, try to understand the experiences of others who have, but are unable to relate to it. They then put the experience with the creative force into terms they can understand, relational terms. They personify the force or parts of it. In the ancient world they may have taken one aspect of the 'Powers,' such as lightning, and made it into a god and personified it, not recognizing that it is only one part of the whole and not the whole or the most powerful part. This then gave rise to superstition, because by not embracing and understanding the whole, the individual parts no longer seem to follow recognizable patterns and in order to understand them, an artificial environment is constructed. This artificial environment is religion.

So what is our proper relation to YHVH? The ability to 'know God' is to be in harmony with the universe, but also brings with it the ability to manipulate the creation. We were infused with this power. The idea that 'YHVH breathed into us,' means that the kinetic energy of the universe is within us. Originally, this meant that the *adam* had the ability to manipulate and control his environment. He was able to be in harmony with all the animals and the garden and all his needs would have been met. After the fall, this was no longer the case, but the potential remained there. Noah had it and recognized that the course of action mankind had taken would result in an imbalance in creation so severe that a catastrophic readjustment would take place. He prepared accordingly. Avraham left the confines of idolatry in Ur and after spending years in the nomadic lifestyle, got in touch with the created order, enough to exercise its power. Apparently he was the first one with the ability to pass this power on to his descendants and with such a power could foresee them being numerous and powerful. The blessing did not cause it, but gave them the ability to see it happen if they used it wisely. He passed this blessing to Yitzach. Ya'akov received it from His father even though it was by deception. It would seem that the passing on of this ability, to be in touch with the creative power of the universe is not always dependent upon righteousness. And the exercise of this power is not always done in a wise way. We have looked at the 'law of unintended consequences' and have seen how both Ya'akov and Yosef exercised this power in a way that was selfish and resulted in negative consequences down the line.

Most translations have 'formed out of the ground' implying a 'cookie cutter' type of formation. We have translated it as 'pressed' in the sense of being forced to move or act from an external force. It is like a man that is driven from his home to a place of refuge. Understood this way, the *adam* was not the first man created, but a man who eventually found refuge in the garden. He was a man on a spiritual journey causing problems with his previous community. This often happens when one goes against the accepted norms and asks all the wrong questions as the character from 'Pilgrim's Progress' found out. He found himself run out of town and forced to become a wanderer, a nomad, where he learned about the breath of YHVH. Incidentally, *adam* may be a place name attached to him and not really his name. He may have been from the multitude of people from *Ha'adamah*. This would explain Cain's reluctance to leave the area immediately outside the garden as others existed who would kill him. This also helps to explain where Cain got his wife. *Adam* was not the only person on earth; just the only one 'enlightened' enough to enter the garden.

The *adam* received a *nesh'mat chayim* from the breath of YHVH the powers. This is a new term, but is similar to our previous *nefesh chayah* of the animals, but *nefesh chayah* is never used to refer to the *adam*. Only animals have *nefesh chayah* and the *adam* exists 'for' them. The *adam* was placed here to be like a king who serves and is served by his subjects, referring back to the previous explanation of his mission to journey, rule and improve. But as we have seen, *nefesh chayah* is not just the animals, but the whole earth; it is shared among all things.

So what is the *nesh'mat chayim*? It is plural which refers either to quantity or quality. Nesh'mat is derived from the same root as *shem*, which is a name or character of something. The *adam* is infused with the character of the powers and since the powers encompass the whole spectrum of creation, both good and evil, darkness and light, we share this dichotomy. Originally these characteristics were in harmony, but the fall brought imbalance. The breath/wind/character of the powers can be used to correct this imbalance or make it worse.

'Chayim' is simply the plural of *chayah* which is life or existence. But this is it not the same as the *chayah* of the animals. The *chayim* come from the powers as well, and is plural just as the word *Elohim* is plural. The *chayah* comes from the earth and is singular and simple. We partake of the plural nature of the powers, the shadow of the *Elohim*. *Chayah* is life force or existence, to be aware. To have more than one *chayah* is to have multiple consciousnesses. Man had the ability to operate on several levels at once: instinct, reason, or emotion. Animals operate according to instinct, they have basic programming. We have the ability to override this basic programming, for good or evil.

This verse concludes; "and the *adam* existed for the *nefesh chayah*." Note that most translations translate this as; "and man became a living being/soul." This translation ignores the grammar of the Hebrew as well as the prefix of the phrase *nefesh chayah* that means 'for.' *Adam* is not 'a' *nefesh chayah*, but he is 'for' the *nefesh chayah*, the animals, confirming our previous statements that *adam* was to journey with and rule over the animals.

Genesis 2:8

וַיִּטַּע יְהוָה אֱלֹהִים גַּן־בְּעֵדֶן מִקֶּדֶם וַיָּשֶׂם שָׁם
אֶת־הָאָדָם אֲשֶׁר יָצָר:

And YHVH the Powers established a protected region in Eden from ancient times. And he placed there the adam whom he molded.

YHVH established a *gan*, translaterd here as a 'protected region[40],' but usually translated as a 'garden.' What is a garden? It is a place where things are grown that is usually protected by some type of wall or barrier and the planting of things within the garden is part of the duty of man. But the duties of man do not end there. The use of the word 'established' refers to more than just the plants but the enclosure and everything else necessary for the garden. The question is; Why is it enclosed? What is separated? What is outside?

Now we can bring into our story some of the speculation we engaged in in verse 5. What was 'outside' was what the *adam* had escaped from or perhaps what he was taken from by YHVH. This means the people of Genesis chapter one and the *adam* are not the same group. When the *adam* was taken from this place he was given the *nesh'mat chayim*. If we look at the story of what happened to Cain after he kills his brother, we can get a good idea of what was outside.

After Cain kills his brother, he goes east of Eden to Nod where he has a son and names the city he founds after him. A city and a region require people and the region he went to, actually the word is

---

[40] The word *gan* is the root of the Hebrew word *magen* meaning 'shield.'

122

'returned to,' was already known and established as Cain was worried that whoever met him would kill him. This only makes sense if people outside his clan existed. In his case, Cain's clan (Adam and his descendants) would have the responsibility of the blood avenger and he should have been more worried about staying than going. He was, however, worried that these people, who lived to the east of the garden, would kill him, even though they would have no way of knowing what he had done. This would mean that they had a reputation for killing in general or killing strangers in particular. Their trend toward violence would be described later in the story of Noah. The mark Cain received must have had superstitious meaning to them and may have prevented them from killing him, perhaps even making him into a leader, as he did establish a city among them. He may also still have had the *nesh'mat chayim*, which would have elevated him and his descendants among the people and the intermixing of blood/*chayim* created the *nephilim*. It was the additional reasoning capabilities and power of the *nesh'mat chayim*, combined with the natural savagery of these people that led to the advanced and blood thirsty race described in Genesis chapter six.

But enough of the outside, what is the protected region like and where was it? Eden was designed to be a place of delight. Man was created to be happy and in a state of pleasure and *shalom*. If the *adam* was taken from another place and brought here, he could appreciate it because it was so much better. Man was not created to suffer and be deprived. Christianity has often equated pleasure with sin and sought to eradicate it. Life as we know it is hard but it was not meant to be so and if we learn to live it as we should, in harmony with our environment and with each other, it will be more like Eden and less like hell. The idea that our life is a punishment for our sin and is to be endured in all its harshness is foolhardy. We were not placed here to passively accept disharmony and pain, but to overcome it, to transform it. Life should be a delight; we should be like a king in his palace. Not hedonistic or devoid of responsibility but active and in balance.

The *Zohar* has some interesting comments on this verse concerning where the *adam* was taken from. It says that the four elements hinted to in this passage, becoming the four heads, refer to levels of spiritual reality. The *adam* could partake of all these levels at once. Whether this was acquired and then brought into the garden or he was created this way in the garden is speculation. That he had heightened awareness is not in doubt. It is only later that the 'higher,' or other levels, became clouded that he, and we, became reduced in our perceptions. If the *adam* did acquire this perception through some effort or life experience on his part and was taken to Eden as a result, it gives a different meaning to our lives and their aim.

When Y'shua taught that the 'Kingdom of Heaven is at hand' or 'all around you' or 'within you,' he may have been referring to this idea that Eden is available to us, not as a physical place on earth or even in 'heaven,' but an ever present reality we just do not perceive. This is not to say that Eden is just a level of consciousness, some mental game. Elijah was taken there bodily, we believe Moshe saw it at the burning bush and could have entered in had he not gone to save his people. If one truly enters Eden, one can leave this reality behind. Or one can operate within both, exercising great power. If Eden and Y'shua's 'Kingdom of heaven' are the same, the 'Holy Spirit' and the *nesh'mat chayim* would be the same and we have a whole new understanding of one of his crucial teachings.

This then gives us an idea of where it is. Most translate the verse 'in the east' but we have 'from ancient times[41].' One of the reasons why is because when the *adam* was thrown out of the garden, he moved to the east, which means the garden would have been to his west, not to the east from his point of reference. Since that doesn't make sense, we went with the alternate translation. In the ancient world, most things were oriented to the east. In the ancient mind the past, not the future, was in front of you as you are able to see the past, but not the future. Therefore, far off in the east was the ancient past. This would mean that the protected place had existed for a long time and may have been known to others besides the *adam* and may one day be known to us.

---

[41] The Hebrew word *qedem* means both, east and ancient.

Genesis 2:9

וַיַּצְמַח יְהוָה אֱלֹהִים מִן־הָאֲדָמָה כָּל־עֵץ נֶחְמָד לְמַרְאֶה וְטוֹב לְמַאֲכָל וְעֵץ הַחַיִּים בְּתוֹךְ הַגָּן וְעֵץ הַדַּעַת טוֹב וָרָע:

And YHVH the Powers grew from the ground all the trees that were pleasing to the sight and good for food, trees of the chayim in the middle of the protected region and the trees of the experience of function and dysfunction.

Once the *adam* is in the protected place, YHVH of the *Elohim* provides for his sustenance. It is more than that however. The trees are not only good for food, they do not just serve the function of sustaining his life physically, but the trees were also pleasing to the eye. The natural world was not just created to be functional but artistically pleasing as well.

These trees are the trees of *chayim* (life) and trees of the experience of function and dysfunction (good and evil). Notice that our translation uses 'trees' rather than 'tree' and this is for several reasons. First, the Hebrew word *eyts* can mean 'tree' or 'trees' as the plural form of this word, *etsim*, is strictly used for 'wood.' Second, the context of the passage does not specifically state there is only one tree of each, rather it implies a grove of each by the use of the phrase 'all the trees." Finally, biologically, there is rarely only one kind of a plant or tree in an area, so it is more than likely there were more than one of each. After all, the purpose of the plants, as stated in chapter one, was to multiply.

What can we tell of the trees from this verse? Let's begin with the trees of *chayim*. This is not the simple *chayah* of the other plants and animals but relates to the *chayim* of the *adam*. The *chayim* of the trees and the *nesh'mat chayim* of the *adam*, both came specifically from YHVH. It could be that the trees gave the same *chayim* that YHVH gives. In Daniel 12:12, the righteous are rewarded with 'everlasting lives' (*chayim*). This state of being in the garden, having not just *chayah*, but *chayim*, is the same as the state of those who are righteous enter into, either here or in the hereafter. Another possibility is the trees actually had, or were, some substance that both rejuvenated the cells, imparting energy to keep them from deteriorating, and led or kept one at a level of higher consciousness. Whichever it was (or some combination of both), the constant importation of *chayim* to the *adam* was part of the experience of the garden. When Y'shua taught that we could have eternal life, he was not talking about some distant hope, but a present experience of a higher state of being available to all who seek it. Eternal life, the Kingdom of God/Heaven and the *nesh'mat chayim* are all interchangeable terms and refer to this state in the garden where one is physically functional in every way and that function is maintained indefinitely and one is of heightened consciousness.

As we have seen throughout our study, one cannot have something on one side without the balance of the other. The balance to the 'trees of life' is the 'trees of the experience of function and dysfunction.' First, to understand these trees, let's take a look at what is described. 'Experience' is our translation of דעת (*da'at*), which comes from the root דע (*da*), which refers to knowledge. To know something in the scriptures is to experience it. For example, in the Bible, to 'know' a woman is to experience her sexually. It is not a simple mental exercise, but an experience of one's whole being. The word דע, or ⊙▽, in the ancient script, is a dalet (a picture of a door) and an ayin (a picture of the eye), so it is understood as the 'door of the eye.' It refers to the way we experience the world, by using our sense of sight as our primary means of obtaining stimuli. This parallels the phrase 'pleasing to the eye' mentioned earlier in this verse. The experience of, or through, the trees is that of *tov*, that which is good, beautiful and functional, and ra'ah, that which is evil, causes pain or is dysfunctional. To partake of these trees is to enter a state in which things are no longer in balance, there are highs and lows, and there is joy and pain and not necessarily in equal proportion.

The trees of life kept things in balance; the experience was one of timeless, functional existence, much like that of *Ayn Soph*. There was no pain in the garden because there was nothing dysfunctional to cause it and the *adam*'s heightened awareness would have kept him from it. Would this be boring? Only to someone who concentrated on the "I" of the ego, someone who saw self and the fulfillment of self as the highest priority. To the *adam* he had his work of maintaining and guarding the garden, expanding creation and maintaining the balance of things. I would not think the job of co-creator/completer would be 'boring.'

Partaking of the trees of the experience of function and dysfunction caused things to be out of balance, beginning with the body. In a very concrete sense, the eating from these trees caused one to become sick, much like when a prophet was told to eat a scroll. The scroll tasted good, the trees were pleasing, but in the stomach it turned sour, it made the body dysfunctional. These trees moved us from our optimal state of being to one driven by ego and separation. We moved away from an intuitive based existence, where we were in touch with the true nature of things and could act accordingly because we were 'plugged in' to the infinite.

Now we are a knowledge based society where our ego controls our actions and our knowledge is limited by our personal experience. If we are to be co-creators/completers and we are limited by our own experience, which is limited by our physical location and lifespan, we have a real problem. We no longer understand how all the pieces fit together. We may attempt to put things together piecemeal, if we even care at all. We puff ourselves up with our knowledge, separate ourselves from one another and fill the gaps in our knowledge with religion, superstition and speculation. And of course, we think that we are right in our knowledge and everyone else is wrong and we twist the truth to fit the agenda we have to fill our egos. This all causes separation between individuals and between man and creation. Separation causes more pain, turmoil and death and in our limitations we can do little about it, even though our ego tells us we can do it all. This is the world we live in.

The choice is ours. We can continue on our path of knowledge and continue to send our society and planet into the toilet or we can seek to eliminate the ego and tap into the infinite, understanding how to bring about balance and acting on it. The opportunity exists for all of us to reach the higher state of being that the *adam* did, this state of eternal life or perhaps better understood as 'life in the eternal,' operating in the state of eternal things. Noah, Avraham, Moshe, the prophets, Y'shua, they all understood this and sought to bring those they knew into this experience. One cannot get there through knowledge, filling up the ego. One needs to let go of one's life, become egoless like a small child and experience the universe as it is, fill ourselves with its eternal nature. The writers of the scripture sought to point the way, but knowledge of it will not get you there. That's what Y'shua told the leaders of his day. They study the scriptures thinking that in them is eternal life. It is not the study that gives eternal life; it is change of one's life and mindset.

Genesis 2:10

וְנָהָר יֹצֵא מֵעֵדֶן לְהַשְׁקוֹת אֶת־הַגָּן וּמִשָּׁם יִפָּרֵד וְהָיָה
לְאַרְבָּעָה רָאשִׁים:

**And a river comes out from eden to give drink to the protected
region and from there it spreads out. And it goes to the four
kings.**

The word for river is *na'ir* which is related to *ner*, light or that which
gives off light. The *ner* is not the light itself but its source and here we
have the source of water itself. It is no accident that the two, water
and light, are related linguistically, since both are essential for life to
exist on Earth. This could also be related to the well or source of water
that followed the Israelites in the desert (just as the pillar of fire
provided light). The river flows out of Eden to water the protected
region/garden and from there goes out and becomes divided into four
rivers that will be named in the next few verses. These regions outside
the protected region are the original four kingdoms, one of which is
perhaps the one that the *adam* came from.

Notice something else in our verse. Eden and the garden are not the
same place. Eden is an area and within that area is the protected
region. The river originates in Eden and flows into the protected
region. This could also be synonymous with the river of life found in
the book of Revelation. Certainly, in a literal sense, it was the river of
life for it provided life giving water to all the plants and animals of the
protected region as well as the regions outside of Eden. In addition to
the mist and geysers, this could be the only source of water that
existed at this time. It would be like the Nile in Egypt or even the Tigris

and Euphrates that are the only dependable source of water in otherwise arid regions.

Genesis 2:11

שֵׁם הָאֶחָד פִּישׁוֹן הוּא הַסֹּבֵב אֵת כָּל־אֶרֶץ הַחֲוִילָה
אֲשֶׁר־שָׁם הַזָּהָב:

The name of the one is Pishon. It is the one that circles around all the land of the Havilah, where the gold is.

The Pishon is the first river mentioned, perhaps because of its importance, maybe because it was closest to Eden. It is the first branch of the river of life. This is where the original civilization of Genesis chapter one started, to the west of Eden. The word *Havilah* , meaning circled one in Hebrew, refers to a people, not a place, because the prefixed letter 'hey,' meaning 'the,' precedes the name making it 'the Havilah,' or 'the circled one.' 'The circled one' specifically refers to an individual, possibly a king who represented his people. This could be the first civilization, the first settlement/city that took people from the nomadic lifestyle and introduced consumerism and a social hierarchy to them, taking them from the intuitive based garden and into the knowledge based urban environment.

There is a parallel between verses five through seven and verses eight through fifteen. The trees, the water and the garden are recurring themes. The rivers are the product of the mist that originally watered things, and the mist was perhaps the product of a geyser whose great volume of water was the source of the four rivers.

Genesis 2:12

וּזְהַב הָאָרֶץ הַהִוא טוֹב שָׁם הַבְּדֹלַח וְאֶבֶן הַשֹּׁהַם:

**And the gold of that land is beautiful. The b'dolach is there
and the shoham stone.**

This verse gives us a short description on the land of the *Pishon* River. It begins with a discussion of the gold of the land. It says that the gold is 'beautiful' which means that it is 'functional.' What is functional about it? Perhaps in this land it was so abundant that it was used for everyday things. It is more than that however. Gold was used throughout the construction of the *Mishkan* and later, the Temple itself. Why? And why is gold considered so precious, just because it's pretty? Who first looked at the yellow rock and thought it was valuable? Could it be that there is a 'spiritual component' to this particular metal? The ark was encased in it, the mercy seat cover was solid gold and it was here that YHVH appeared to Moshe and the High Priest. It could very well be that gold has some property within its atomic structure that enables us to see into the 'spiritual realm' much like uranium has within its atomic makeup the capacity to produce power. This idea, begun in the distant past, could be the reason why so many religious traditions use gold in their idols and religious practices.

The next thing found in this land is *b'dolach*. This is a resin and the only other place we find this word used in the scriptures is in Numbers 11:7 where it is said that manna is like it. Could this be a basic food for the people of this land? It sustained the people of Israel for years in the desert so it must be a 'complete' food, containing all the necessary vitamins and minerals, proteins, fats and carbohydrates the human body needs.

Finally, the stone of the *shoham* is here. These stones were an essential piece of the costume of the High Priest. Two of them were placed on his shoulders and were engraved with the names of the sons of Israel as well as being part of the ephod. If you look at the Hebrew of our verse, you will note it is singular, 'the *shoham* stone.' It is a specific stone and we can infer from its use by the High Priest, a stone of spiritual significance. Stone/rock is used in reference to spiritual things throughout the scriptures. The 'rock' begets Israel and carries him through the wilderness[42]. YHVH is described as a rock many times. In fact, Jewish tradition says that there was a rock that went with Israel through the desert, just as the well and the pillar of fire and cloud did. Rocks were significant signposts that marked places geographically[43]. Y'shua said that Peter was a rock and there is a rock that smashes Nebuchadnezzar's idol. Could all this imagery be related to the significance of the *shoham* stone?

We believe all these items are significant, not just a physical description of the land, but of its function. This land was the gateway to Eden. Avraham left Ur to seek the promises of God. The *adam* may have done the same thing and this was the last stop on the journey before he reached it. Everything he needed to attain *neshemah* and gain entrance was here: the gold for getting in touch with that dimension, the *b'dolach* to sustain him with little work required and the *shoham* stone to show him the way. This place is the highest state of man in his natural state. Avraham, Moshe, the prophets, Y'shua, they all represent a higher level, the level of the *neshemah*. This is eternal life, being connected to the eternal things. How did Y'shua answer the question of 'how do I attain eternal life?' He said two things: first, follow the commandments by which we establish

---

[42] Deuteronomy 32:18
[43] See Judges 20:47

harmony with our fellow man and the world around us, and second, give up your possessions. The latter has to do with eliminating the ego for it is in our possessions that we identify ourselves. We need to become unattached to such things and their accumulation. The nomadic lifestyle of the patriarchs and prophets teaches us this[44]. Once we learn such things we receive/attain the *neshemah*/higher consciousness and enter the garden where we want for nothing and can cultivate the state of 'no-mind.' 'Knowledge' which is necessary for survival outside the garden, and is too often used to feed the ego, is no longer necessary. In this place we have everything we need and can concentrate on that which we were created for.

---

[44] See appendix (The Nomadic Lifestyle).

Genesis 2:13

וְשֵׁם־הַנָּהָר הַשֵּׁנִי גִּיחוֹן הוּא הַסּוֹבֵב אֵת כָּל־אֶרֶץ כּוּשׁ:

And the name of the second river is Gihon. It is the one that circles around the land of Cush.

Gihon means to surround and it surrounds the land of Cush, meaning black and was later associated with Ethiopia.

Genesis 2:14

וְשֵׁם הַנָּהָר הַשְּׁלִישִׁי חִדֶּקֶל הוּא הַהֹלֵךְ קִדְמַת אַשּׁוּר
וְהַנָּהָר הָרְבִיעִי הוּא פְרָת:

And the name of the third river is Hiddekel. It is the one that walks the ancient path. And the fourth river, it is the Parat.

Hidekel has the meaning of a rapid step, which obviously refers to walking, or taking a journey. *Asshur*, usually translated as 'Assyria' is the ancient path. *Asshur* comes from the root *asher* which is a rope that brings things together and since the rope is usually taut, it is also something straight. The 'ancient path' is the one that sees the connection of all things, they are *echad*. This is the awakening necessary to move onto the path, to begin the journey to the actual experience of God.

The final river is the *Parat*. *Parat* means fruitfulness so the land apparently produced abundantly. This is the only river that has no additional information included, it just is. This one needs no explanation because it conforms to our present reality, it is what we all experience, it is already familiar. In order to move on past this place one has to recognize the simplicity of life or to make his life simple like the nomad, in order to begin the journey.

The rivers point our way to Eden, they are steps along the way. We can think of the rivers more along the lines of concentric circles around Eden, each river inside the one before. We can see by the names of the rivers that they are a road to the garden. We begin with *Parat*, equated with fruitfulness and the earth. The fruitful place is where one learns to live in harmony with the world. From here we move on to *Hidekel*, which literally means 'rapid' and is equated with 'fire.' This is the realization that the mind fires rapidly out of control and needs to be brought into line. This is the first step on the journey and where we become refined like fire. We have left the comforts of our daily existence and will experience the disapproval of those around us who choose not to begin the journey. This desire, to move out of *Parat*, brings the mind under control and causes one to forgo the consumer mentality, for the nomadic lifestyle will quickly put one at odds with the dominate society.

The next stop along the journey is the *Gihon* in the land of *Cush*. *Gihon* means surround and is equated with water and *Cush* means black. Both water and blackness are symbols of chaos. Chaos is nothingness; it is the lack of ego, a state of no-thought. This is where things begin to get really serious. Once one can control the mind one can enter into a state of no-mind/thought. Then one can move on to *Pishon* which literally means 'scatter' and is equated with the wind. This is where one realizes and connects with the scattering of the elemental power that is in all things and then receives/attains the *ruach*/wind/*neshamah*. This is also where the *shoham* stone is, which is the recognition that all things are *echad*. Once this happens, one becomes *echad* with the universe and enters Eden and the garden.

Genesis 2:15

וַיִּקַּח יְהוָה אֱלֹהִים אֶת־הָאָדָם וַיַּנִּחֵהוּ בְגַן־עֵדֶן לְעָבְדָהּ
וּלְשָׁמְרָהּ:

**And YHVH the Powers took the adam and he settled him in
the protected region of Eden to work her and to protect her.**

This verse gets us back to our narrative. There is a question as to why
the author interrupted the narrative with the information about the
rivers and the surrounding land. The information, whether
geographical, spiritual, or both, certainly helps the context of the
story, but its insertion in the middle of the narrative is unexplained.

We use the word 'settled' for the *adam*, not only because that is part
of the meaning of this word, but because it encompasses our whole
idea of the *adam* attaining the goal of his journey. Like the pioneers of
the American west, the *adam* had endured to the end and now he can
settle down, relax, enjoy the fruits of his hard work. He had been led
there by YHVH the powers and now he could settle down and
establish himself in his work.

What was his work? We had previously established that the work of
man is to complete the creation. The work of the *adam* is more
specific in this verse and relates directly to the garden. He is to 'work
her and protect her.' These two things go hand in hand. But you may
be wondering, from what is the *adam* to protect her from? There are
several possibilities but we will focus on two. The first is that he was to
serve as the gatekeeper for this place of rest. Eden, and the garden
within, was not just a place of higher consciousness, but also a real
geographical location. It could be that the *adam* was to make sure that
those who sought to enter as he did actually belonged there. After he

blew it, YHVH placed a cherubim with a flaming sword at the entrance to do the same.

The second thing the *adam* could be protecting the garden from was the infusion of chaos. In the garden everything was in perfect balance and it was the *adam*'s job to keep it that way, he protected the balance. He was in training to do the same for the rest of creation, remembering the previous chapter and the duty of man to complete creation and to keep balance. The 'Genesis chapter one man' failed in that duty and in 'the *adam*' YHVH the powers saw someone who may be able to be trained to do it successfully. The garden then becomes a microcosm of all of creation. Avraham, Moshe, the prophets and Y'shua all came to do and teach the same thing: how man could bring about balance in his world both socially and physically. Each showed the way past the sword to the trees of life. Each community had the opportunity to develop a place where this happened, enter or create Eden and the garden and then be a light to individuals and nations as to how things were meant to be.

The work, therefore, was real work and it was work for someone else, in this case YHVH. Everything in the garden was as it should be, the balance was there, the *adam* merely had to maintain it. One of the reasons it was so crucial was the nature of the creation itself. As we have described it, there has been an evolution of responsibility in the creative process. It began with *Ayn Soph*, was passed to the *Elohim* then to the earth itself and now it has come to man. The *Elohim* have completed their part and are finished as active participants in the creative process. As entities created by *Ayn Soph*, entities often associated with physical phenomena, they are now subject to decay (second law of thermodynamics). That being the case, the *Elohim* in cooperation with *Ayn Soph* created man for their own preservation. Man was supposed to be the one to continually put energy into the system so it would go on. Unfortunately, man failed and then even the *adam* failed and everything will continue its slide into chaos and the nothingness that was before.

Genesis 2:16

וַיְצַו יְהוָה אֱלֹהִים עַל־הָאָדָם לֵאמֹר מִכֹּל עֵץ־הַגָּן אָכֹל
תֹּאכֵל:

**And YHVH the Powers commanded over the man saying,
"from all the trees of the protected region you will utterly
devour."**

The first word in this verse is the verb *tsavah*, which is often translated as 'command.' In the ancient script the root of this word is written as Ψℎ. The letter ℎ represents a trail and the letter Ψ represents a man with his arms raised up in revelation. From these pictures we find the definition 'the trail to revelation.' This could be interpreted a couple of ways. First, YHVH provides the trail of revelation to the food while the second interpretation may be that the food YHVH gives puts us on the trail of revelation. The foods that we consume can be helpful to us or they can be detrimental. Isaiah 7:15 tells us that 'he will eat curds and dates in order that he will know to refuse the evil and choose the good. We have all heard the expression, 'You are what you eat,' but maybe this is true on a spiritual level as well as a physical one.

The word *akal*, meaning 'eat,' is found at the end of the sentence and is doubled for emphasis. This is a command to eat, to sustain the body. To those who embark on the journey, the ascetic lifestyle may be appealing and certainly there is a place for it at times, but one should not neglect the physical for the 'spiritual' because they are intertwined. It is difficult to concentrate on 'spiritual' things when one's body is unhealthy or uncomfortable. It is interesting that eating has a negative connotation to us in this verse for to eat is to devour and destroy. But it is just a fact that what we eat is destroyed, broken down into its basic components, which we then use to fuel our bodies.

Genesis 2:17

וּמֵעֵץ הַדַּעַת טוֹב וָרָע לֹא תֹאכַל מִמֶּנּוּ כִּי בְּיוֹם אֲכָלְךָ
מִמֶּנּוּ מוֹת תָּמוּת:

"And from the trees of the experience of function and dysfunction you will not eat from them because in the day you eat from them, a death you will die."

There is an interesting parallel in our verse and it concerns eating and death. In the previous verse we mentioned that eating has a negative connotation and here it is paralleled with *mot* or death. In the act of eating we destroy our food; we break it down into simpler components that are completely unrecognizable from the original. The fact is that when anything dies, the process of decomposition followed by the use of the broken down components by other living things, make it unrecognizable as well.

What did this warning mean to the *adam*? If he was created in the garden and the garden was perfectly harmonious, what would he have understood of death? Most traditions do not have him in the garden very long, some only a day. Certainly he would not have experienced anything dying in so short a time. If one does not understand the consequences, the warning means little. Just as you may tell a child not to go near a hot stove or he will burn himself, if he's never been burnt, he can't put the warning into context, it won't be truly meaningful. Once he feels the heat and becomes uncomfortable, only then does he begin to understand.

If, however, as we have theorized, the *adam* came from outside the garden, worked his way through the various 'kingdoms' of the rivers, he would have had a very good idea of what death was like. He had seen it and understood it. 'Dust to dust' was exactly what was warned of in the command. His being was the result of a particular combination of basic components, molecules and atoms, and at death his being would be reduced to those components again. But in the garden that wouldn't happen. He had found eternal life. He was in a unique place where the law of decay was constantly offset by the constant importation of new life and energy. To the *adam*, the threat was very real.

He was given a choice of two paths. The first was the path represented by the trees of life, which were found in the garden, a perfect, balanced, harmonious existence where he worked with the *Elohim* to fulfill his purpose. The second was represented by the trees of the knowledge of function and dysfunction. In reality, it was all based on his perception and interaction with his surroundings. The natural world does not have a distinction between function and dysfunction. It operates according to law, things unfold as they should, they are always functional. It is we who place moral value on the way it acts according to those laws because of the way it affects us. Everything from earthquakes to viruses are simply natural phenomenon acting according to law. When we go against that law, try to change the world around us that is when the effects are negative. If one builds a house in a place known to have earthquakes or at the foot of a volcano, then there will eventually be negative consequences, particularly if one is no longer attuned to nature and its signs. The animals seem to know when an earthquake is coming and volcanoes don't just blow up without any warning. But we choose to ignore them because we have invested in our homes and possessions and are loath to uproot ourselves, the complete opposite of a nomad who will easily move in plenty of time. He will not stay and starve when there is a drought or an infestation. He takes care of himself so viruses have no hold. So much sickness is caused by the environment we create for ourselves and by what we put into our bodies. It was the unsanitary conditions in so many cities that lead to disease and plague; it is altering the chemical makeup of our bodily systems with so many synthetics that makes us susceptible to disease and the deterioration of our systems. This is all the result of our ego and our ignorance of how to be at harmony with the world around us. We think we can change the world for the better; we can 'improve' on the natural balance to satisfy our ego and appetites. But it only makes things worse and one thing compounds on another in ways we could not foresee. And at the end, we die and return to the dust from which we emerged.

While our translation of this verse includes the phrase "you will not eat from them" an alternate translation is "you will not eat from us" as the Hebrew word *mimenu* can be translated as "from them" or "from us." With this translation it means *Elohim* and YHVH are equated with the trees of good and bad. It is interesting to note that in Genesis 3:5 God says that if they eat from the trees of good and bad they will be like *Elohim* (the powers).

Genesis 2:18

וַיֹּאמֶר יְהוָה אֱלֹהִים לֹא־טוֹב הֱיוֹת הָאָדָם לְבַדּוֹ
אֶעֱשֶׂה־לּוֹ עֵזֶר כְּנֶגְדּוֹ:

And YHVH the Powers said, "It is not good for the existence of the adam to be alone, I will provide for him a helper like his story."

This verse shows that creation is an ongoing process, as we have stated previously. Even in the garden, there are things lacking, in this case, the *adam* was not complete, he needed a helper like him and according to his story. The *adam* came into the garden alone, no one was worthy to come with him. No one had come this far on the journey with him; no one had a story like his. If he was a preacher of righteousness along the way, he apparently had as much success bringing people to a higher spiritual level as did Noah or many of the other prophets.

The *adam* had gone on this journey and no one made it to the end with him. He had no doubt become self reliant, used to being alone. It is not apparent from our verse that he felt the lack of companionship, perhaps he thought, as many do who hold fast to a course which few if any understand, that being alone was better. Or he was not as perceptive to his needs as he should have been, he was still learning and growing, even in the garden. YHVH understood the need, however. Man was created male and female for a reason, they were not meant to be separated. They were supposed to journey together. Perhaps he had a companion who did not dedicate herself to the journey and was left behind. Y'shua said as much when he stated that he brought a sword to households and some would lose families on the way. But man is a social creature; it is not good for him to be alone. The life of a hermit may serve its purpose on a temporary basis, but it is not meant to be the rule. It could well be that he needed a companion to continue his journey. Once the question was posed, 'Can one sin, or grow, in isolation?' Mental ideas of sin aside, if there is no one to perform either good or bad deeds for, how can one move morally one way or the other? The *adam* needed a companion to continue his journey. At the very least, he needed a honey to put together his 'honey do' list for the garden!

Genesis 2:19

וַיִּצֶר יְהוָה אֱלֹהִים מִן־הָאֲדָמָה כָּל־חַיַּת הַשָּׂדֶה וְאֵת
כָּל־עוֹף הַשָּׁמַיִם וַיָּבֵא אֶל־הָאָדָם לִרְאוֹת מַה־יִּקְרָא־לוֹ
וְכֹל אֲשֶׁר יִקְרָא־לוֹ הָאָדָם נֶפֶשׁ חַיָּה הוּא שְׁמוֹ׃

And YHVH the Powers pressed out from Ha'adamah all the chayah of the field and all the flyers of the skies. And He(YHVH) came to the adam to see who he would call to himself, and all that he will call to himself, the adam of nefesh, that will become his character/breath.

This verse tells us a lot about man and God and the world around us. It begins the creation of new animals for the garden. Like the *adam* in a previous verse, the animals were 'pressed out,' they came from *Ha'adamah* to the garden. They could have come from the same place as the *adam*. Because of the similarity to the *adam*, we can probably associate some degree of consciousness to the animals created in this verse. Like the *adam*, they were different from the others previously created. Perhaps something had happened to their kind outside the garden, the men who were not fulfilling their proper role in the world may have done something to keep them from fulfilling their purpose as well. They may have been brought to the garden for the same reason the *adam* was, to create one place of harmony where everything was in balance.

Now we must get back to the purpose for this little exercise. It is apparent from our context that he needs help in the garden, either with his work, his journey or both. So YHVH brings the animals to him to see which he would find suitable, which he would 'call to himself.' If you are still holding on to a traditional western view of God, there are some things here that don't make any sense. First of all, why would an *omnipotent* God make man with an obvious deficiency? According to the traditional view, God created Adam, placed him in the garden with a task to perform and then, oops, found out he couldn't do it alone. Realizing his mistake, this *omniscient* God now has to figure out how to help man out, so through the process of *trial and error*, he looks for a suitable helper. An all powerful, all knowing God would not have created man with such a deficiency nor would he have to go through an experimental process to fix it. There are many places in the scriptures where such a God makes little sense and often makes him appear petty, indecisive and unjust. If we instead begin to understand that such personification of the eternal is simply a literary device, used by those who have experienced the eternal, to explain it to those who have not, then it makes the scriptures and man's interaction with the divine within it much more believable and comprehensible.

So why does the *adam* need a helper? The act of bringing animals rules out propagation as well as the fact that if the *adam* had found the source of eternal life, the need for the next generation would not have been pressing. The question was answered in our previous verse; he needed someone like 'his story.' He needed someone to share the journey with, someone to share his experiences with, to teach and to learn from. It was the need for social interaction. It is then fair to ask the question 'why bring animals?' Aside from the fact that many find companionship in their pets, there is much more to it than that and it tells us about the unique conditions that existed in the garden.

The animals in our verse were like the *adam* in the sense they came to the garden the same way, they were 'pressed out.' This means that in some sense they share the unique journey that the *adam* did. He was looking for the one whom he could call to himself. To that one he would impart his *neshamah*, just as Y'shua breathed on those who

150

were with him to give them of his 'spirit.' He would elevate them to that higher level of consciousness that would make them 'suitable.' The animals were not made in the 'shadow' of *Elohim* and the *Ayn Soph*, but they did have *nefesh* and were similar in many respects. Having that 'shadow' gave him the unique capacity to impart an 'evolutionary' leap to whichever he found proper. They would then become 'his character/breath' or as he would say in a later verse 'one flesh.'

This all presupposes an important fact; the *adam* could communicate with the animals. This was not, as popular conception would have it, the *adam* sitting on a rock as the animals went by and saying 'aardvark,' 'platypus,' 'giraffe,' 'cockroach,' and so on. To name something in Hebrew culture is to understand its character and function. It would have taken some time for the *adam* to spend enough time with each animal, communicate with it in some way and then ascertain whether or not it would do as a 'helper.' This communication could be a result of the *adam*'s enlightenment or even the ability of the animals in that unique place.

Even though the idea of 'naming' the animals does not really appear in our translation, I think we can discuss it. The idea of 'naming' things is to create an illusion by attaching a symbol to it. We believe that if we can name something, if we can explain it with words, then it becomes real, then we understand it. If we look at that on which one sits and we call it a 'chair' we think we know all there is to know. But we know that isn't true. As the saying goes 'a picture is worth a thousand words' the picture itself is only a symbol of the reality. If one goes on vacation and takes a picture of a sunset on the beach, it does not capture the reality of the experience, only a small visual snapshot that excludes much more than it captures. The immediate experience of standing on the beach, feeling the wind and sand, smelling the salt air, hearing the crash of the waves and the birds overhead cannot be captured by the picture or any description of it. It is a unique experience that is there one moment and never repeated or recaptured. Saying 'I saw a sunset at the beach' may bring up similar memories in others but they are not the same nor will they ever do justice to the experience.

The key is to move beyond the language and symbols we have created and experience the world as it really is. We need to drop our preconceived ideas about things and experience things as they really are. The naming of each animal is not a process of Adam labeling things with symbols but experiencing them in their real state. He didn't simply see an animal and say 'lion' or 'lizard' or 'locust.' He used all his senses to experience the animal for what it was. He did not limit himself by symbols or the ideas he created in his mind. The symbols we create feed on themselves and lead to assumptions that serve to build the illusion and further limit the reality. We have all had experiences where our mind ran off on its own, where we worried incessantly about something in the future (which is by definition an illusion) and heaped possibility on assumption until we were nearly paralyzed. It is all caused by leaving the present reality as it truly exists and creating an illusion, good or bad, that our mind uses to replace what truly exists. And if that wasn't bad enough, in the western world we have replaced our reality further by living vicariously through other people, namely those we see on the television or read in books.

Genesis 2:20

וַיִּקְרָא הָאָדָם שֵׁמוֹת לְכָל־הַבְּהֵמָה וּלְעוֹף הַשָּׁמַיִם וּלְכֹל חַיַּת הַשָּׂדֶה וּלְאָדָם לֹא־מָצָא עֵזֶר כְּנֶגְדּוֹ:

And the adam met the characters/breaths belonging to all the walkers, and to the flyers of the skies and to all the chayah of the field. And for adam no helper was found like his story.

The depth of interaction and understanding reached between the animals and the *adam*, the ability to meet their 'breath,' is beyond the ability of most of us, they are usually hidden from us. But amidst all this effort and time, no suitable helper was found for the *adam*, he found no one to whom he could give his breath. Part of the nature of the universe is to give, just as *Ayn Soph* gave originally. The *adam* could find no one suitable to give to.

Let's talk about 'his story.' What is the essence of this? We have mentioned the fact that his story is like his journey, but it is more than that. It is our journey, our life and all that happens within it that makes us who we are. Our story results in our character and could very well be equated with it. There has always been the question of nature versus nurture, but the reality is while we may have predispositions, it is our environment and the choices we make and the places those choices take us that make us who we are. Every interest we take up, everything we learn, every person we interact with has some effect on who we are and who we are becoming. The *adam* had taken a difficult journey and had no doubt made many sacrifices to get to this point and he desired to impart that to someone. No one fit the bill at this point.

Genesis 2:21

וַיַּפֵּל יְהוָה אֱלֹהִים תַּרְדֵּמָה עַל־הָאָדָם וַיִּישָׁן וַיִּקַּח אַחַת
מִצַּלְעֹתָיו וַיִּסְגֹּר בָּשָׂר תַּחְתֶּנָּה׃

**And YHVH the Powers fell as a trance on the adam and he
slept. And he took a unity from his tzel'ot and he closed flesh
under it.**

The sleep here is more than just sawing logs, something profound and
amazing happens in this verse and it shows the power and potential of
every human being. Notice that YHVH the powers 'is' the trance that
fell on the *adam*. What does this mean? The *adam* entered into a
tardeymah (meditative state)[45] that was like being enveloped and
filled with YHVH. The profound nature of this state has been entered
into by others in the scriptures, but the power exhibited in this
instance is amazing.

In the previous verses we said that the *adam* was looking for someone
or something into which he could impart his *neshemah*, which is what
YHVH the *Elohim* had done to him. Now he takes that one step
further. In this verse he takes his character and breath and forms a
person. Through his connection with the infinite, his elimination of
mind and the wisdom of the universe at his disposal, he was able to
duplicate himself as a unity and not lose anything. He took it from his
tzela, which is traditionally translated as 'rib,' but more literally means
'side.' He duplicated all the important sides of himself, his character,
his 'story.' This was the only suitable helper.

---

[45] See also Genesis 15:12

Genesis 2:22

וַיִּבֶן יְהוָה אֱלֹהִים אֶת־הַצֵּלָע אֲשֶׁר־לָקַח מִן־הָאָדָם
לְאִשָּׁה וַיְבִאֶהָ אֶל־הָאָדָם:

**And YHVH the Powers rebuilt the tzela that he took from the
adam for a woman and she came to the adam.**

The *adam* has formed a facsimile of himself, now YHVH the powers
finishes the job. We all know that it is just one chromosome that
determines sex, the 'X' or 'Y.' YHVH took the essence of what the
adam was and 'tweaked' it a little, enough to make a woman. There is
an interesting possibility as to where the woman came from described
in this language. Could this be a case of cloning? We know that the
technology for cloning exists today as well as the manipulation of the
genetic code. The assumption is that since this was far back in history,
such technology wasn't available. The fact is, an 'ancient time' does
not mean technologically deficient. We still haven't figured out how
the pyramids were built or how Europe, when it was coming out of the
dark ages, 'rediscovered' the technology and knowledge of the
'ancient' Greeks and Romans.

The clone would take time but there is nothing in the story to indicate
the passage of time. There is also a scriptural tradition of marrying
within the clan. Avraham married his half sister, the children of Adam
and Eve married their brothers and sisters, and in this case, *adam*
married himself, his clone. The 'side,' in this case, would have been his
DNA and the Powers would have 'rebuilt' it to make a female. By
having a clone of himself in his high spiritual state, he would have had
a clone with the *neshemah* and his other positive qualities.

Speculation aside, the search is now complete; he had now found someone to give his breath/essence to, almost like sleeping beauty.

The phrase 'for a woman' implies a plan or intent to do something. She was created for a specific purpose, as we know, to be a helper for the *adam*. Interestingly, she was called *ishah* before man was ever called *ish*, both of which come from the word *esh* meaning fire. It could very well be that the *adam* didn't need physical help in the garden, but motivation. He needed someone to light a fire under him to do his work. That may sound humorous, but it is the woman in the house that provides the motivation for 'nesting' and motivating a man to labor in order to provide a suitable home environment in which the woman can raise children and continue the species. Otherwise, the man will live in a slovenly 'bachelor pad' and never move up.

'She came to the *adam*' could have several meanings. The first is that they became one flesh; their essence became one through the sexual act. This is simply recognizing the fact that when two people were married in the ancient Hebrew culture, this was the act that sealed it, just as Isaac went into Rebekah's tent and they were married. No ceremony to speak of, just a singular act that was recognized by the community. In any case, there was no community in the garden to go on ceremony, so this was all there was, an understanding between the two of them. The second is that if she was a clone, she was now old enough to come to the *adam* and YHVH the powers brought her to him. The other possibility is that she came from the same place as the *adam*, and YHVH the powers took his spirit and found a suitable woman outside the garden, filled her with it and brought her into the garden. This possibility eliminates some of the questions of the miraculous from the story and would then make her more 'according to his story.' Regardless, now they are together.

Genesis 2:23

וַיֹּאמֶר הָאָדָם זֹאת הַפַּעַם עֶצֶם מֵעֲצָמַי וּבָשָׂר מִבְּשָׂרִי
לְזֹאת יִקָּרֵא אִשָּׁה כִּי מֵאִישׁ לֻקֳחָה־זֹּאת:

**And the adam spoke this poem, "bone from my bone and flesh
from my flesh." Because of this he will meet woman because
from the man she had received this.**

Ishah is finished, complete in form and function, and if our previous
musings are correct, the test run has been very successful. He is one
with her and knows that this is the suitable helper; she is what YHVH
and he have been looking for. This could also be the origins of the
taboo on bestiality and homosexuality. It is a woman that is to meet
the needs of man in all ways and any other attempt is distorted and
unnatural. It could also be why the family name and inheritance are
reckoned through the man.

The word *pa'am* is like the beating of a drum or a rhythm, which is
why we have translated it as 'poem.' It also hints at the rhythm, the
synchronization between a man and a woman in their lives when they
come together in mutual affection. Those who have been married for
any length of time know that there is a certain rhythm to a
relationship, a pattern, the ability to anticipate one another's needs
and desires, and even the ability to know what the other is thinking
without having to say a word. The *adam* may have known some of this
is his previous life outside the garden, but with one like 'his story' and
sharing the *neshemah*, it was better than he could have imagined.

This is the first recorded conversation so here would be a good time to
discuss language and communication. We have used two important
terms to describe the *adam*'s conversation. First, in our translation we

describe what the *adam* said as a "poem." The second is that we have translated what he was looking for as someone with "his story," in fact, his life experience. Even though we have what we consider a "normal" conversation here, the communication between the man and the woman was very different than that which we usually experience. It is the difference between using language to impart information, and the communication of experience.

Symbols and experience do not follow the same rules of logic. Symbols are the method we usually use to communicate with one another. We use some form of language whether it be that of words, hieroglyphics, body language, or mathematics. The reality is, however, symbols are not a substitute for reality as much as we try to believe they are. We may use a lot of words or pictures to describe something but the words and pictures are not 'it.' I may describe a sunset to you, I may even show you a picture, but neither is 'it,' neither is reality. I may describe an emotion like the 'elation' I felt when my football team won a close game, but as much as I may try to describe my feeling, you will not get 'it.' The truth is that unless you have the experience, there is no real understanding.

Unfortunately western thought does not work this way. We live with the illusion of 'objective reality' and the belief that the symbols we use accurately describe it in ways that anyone should be able to understand, as long as they understand the symbols. Scientists, educators, historians and theologians all operate under the assumption that there is some reality that exists outside of us that can be accurately described by whatever symbols (language) we use. We have been told that everything is one way or the other, that only two real options exist. This is the world of symbols. We all know, however, that is not true. We cannot completely and accurately convey the experience of something through language, like a sunset or happiness or fun. To experience a sunset, you have to be there and even then, no one's experience will be exactly the same. When we try to communicate an idea, whether it is scientific, theological or philosophical, what we hope for is that moment when the light comes on for the listener. That is enlightenment, that is when the idea becomes part of the listener's experience. It is when we have all said 'ah-ha,' when we finally 'get it.'

The best teachers are really poets. It is artistic language which is the best conveyer of our experience. It is the use of analogy or stories or word pictures that assist us in incorporating symbols and concepts into experience. Y'shua knew this, which is why he taught in parables and why throughout the Scriptures, poetic language is used. It is only by understanding the limits of language, a difficult thing in our highly technical society, that we will really learn to communicate with one another. The *adam* and the woman were communicating on a level far beyond that of mere symbols and language. Only if we are fortunate enough to have a friend or spouse with whom we have shared a significant part of our lives with, can we begin to understand what was going on here.

The poem itself makes reference to two things, the bone and the flesh. The bone is the essence of something. We still use the expression 'feeling it deep in my bones' to describe something that happens deep in our being. Ishah was formed from the essence of the *adam*, who he was in 'breath' and *neshemah*. Man was/is made with both masculine and feminine sides/qualities. In men, the masculine side is emphasized physically through the production of testosterone as well as psychologically though our culture. The *tzela* or side or breath of man was taken, copied, and then rebuilt to emphasize the feminine side. One of the reasons for this is that without anyone to share the work load, the *adam*'s masculine and feminine sides were equal in importance and duty and they were like mud, water and dirt all mixed up and useless. True equality, duty and decision making rarely work, something needed to be dominate. By taking the feminine side out (not eliminating it, but de-emphasizing it), it allowed the *adam* to have a dominate side and accomplish his work. The mud was separated; the water could be drunk and the dirt productive.

The next phrase, 'because of this,' is a reference to the fact that the woman has the *tzela* of the man. Something has been taken from him and with the joining of the man and woman; he is now complete once again. We have emphasized many times throughout the story that although things may be separated they are really a unity. A man and a woman complete and complement each other in a partnership, when either of them is alone, he or she is incomplete.

The *adam* is called *ish* for the first time here. Again we may ask ourselves, why is man and woman referred to with a word whose root is 'fire'? In the ancient world, man saw the earth as being composed of four elements: earth, water, wind and fire. Man had been formed of these things with the exception of one. He was formed of the dust of the ground, the earth; much of his body, and specifically his blood, is made of water (chaos); and he received the breath, or wind, from YHVH. From whence comes the fire? Woman. The fire is the fire of passion, not just sexual passion but the whole bundle of emotions that will only exist in the presence of other people. Joy, anger, love, frustration, and all our other emotions need other people with whom to share them. As we said before, a man alone cannot sin. On the positive side, a man also needs someone to share his story with. Our fire, both good and bad, is revealed through others. Land without water is barren, breath without fire is cold and harsh, and a man without passion or emotion is really lifeless. Eastern cultures understand this; they are a passionate and emotional people. We in

160

the west would do well to learn not to 'bottle it up,' but to release our fire before it goes out.

Our translation reads, 'from the man she had received this' because just as creation was brought forth from the essence of *Ayn Soph* and the *Elohim*, so to, the woman was brought forth from the essence of the *adam* by receiving his *tzela*. In this narrative the pattern of separating and filling continues as the feminine is 'separated' out and when the two come together they are 'filled' by becoming whole and functional.

Some may point to Genesis 4:1, after the fall, as the consummation of this 'marriage' when it states that the *adam* 'knew' Eve. However, the grammatical construction of this phrase is the past perfect, and should be translated as 'the *adam* had known Eve,' implying that their union had occurred prior to their exit from the garden.

Genesis 2:24

עַל־כֵּן יַעֲזָב־אִישׁ אֶת־אָבִיו וְאֶת־אִמּוֹ וְדָבַק בְּאִשְׁתּוֹ וְהָיוּ
לְבָשָׂר אֶחָד:

Therefore man will leave his father and his mother and he will join in his woman and they will become unified flesh.

The idea of a recognized union between a man and a woman is codified in this verse. The sexual act itself establishes this unity of the two parts of humanity and this unity is sanctified in what we now call marriage.

That there is some communal or social event marking the first time a man and woman come together and that they are now a unified pair shows the importance of the sexual act itself. It is, first and foremost, a spiritual thing. It is an act designed to strip away all our ego and thoughts to a point where we concentrate only on the moment, the present reality, for that is really the only reality. That is why temple prostitution was a recognized feature of so many pagan cults. It wasn't just so the boys could go have a good time, but because of the inherent spiritual power in the sexual act. It is also why it becomes one of the most regulated activities in the *Torah*. It is a power that is meant to be confined and limited within a family group. Although the *Torah* allows polygamy, Y'shua made it clear that this was not the original intent, that it was to be a bond shared between one man and one woman, a place of safety and intimacy and trust. The *Torah* recognized that the breach of that trust is a very serious matter, one of life and death.

For two people who did not have parents and were not yet parents, the statement 'will leave his father and mother' would have been a difficult concept for them to understand. But of course, the hypothesis put forth by the authors encounters no difficulty here. They had parents, they had some concept of the family unit although what corruption had crept in by this time, outside the garden, we do not know. There may even have been some concept of marriage. It is doubtful that such an idea would have originated here if there were people created in chapter one from whom our protagonists descended. What is clear from our text is that the unity and the creation of a new family unit are crucial in the relationship of man and woman.

Genesis 2:25

וַיִּהְיוּ שְׁנֵיהֶם עֲרוּמִּים הָאָדָם וְאִשְׁתּוֹ וְלֹא יִתְבֹּשָׁשׁוּ׃

And the two of them were enlightened beings, the adam and his woman, and they were not disappointed in each other.

The idea that they were naked or bare has little to do with clothing. In the ancient pictographs, the word for naked (*arom*) could be translated as 'experience the height.' This has to do primarily with their state of being, not their lack of clothing. It is a state of pure experience, living each moment to the fullest with little or no concern for the past or future. The past and future are just figments of our imagination, they exist only in our minds. The only true reality is the moment, what is happening right now. Job 1:21 says 'I came out of the womb naked.' Babies are like this. They have no knowledge; their lives are purely based on the experience of the moment. In addition, Y'shua said that we were to become like little children. Little children have no developed egos; they live for the moment with little concern for their surroundings. They experience life as it comes, they do not try to analyze it or categorize it. They laugh and cry when the situation warrants it regardless of the social circumstances. They live life to the fullest, experiencing and embracing the highs and the lows, and they are our example.

The word *bosh* is usually translated 'ashamed' and has the literal meaning of something that is dry, withered or stinky. We have translated it as 'disappointed' because that is what happens when the spirit dries up. The opposite was true for these two. It is an attempt by the narrator to explain that the state in the garden was anything but disappointing. Because our society, as well as all modern societies, place such a value on the ego, the idea that you are who you think you are, the thought that one could be fulfilled without such self-identity, may be questionable. Y'shua taught that we were to 'deny ourselves' and 'take up our cross.' The elimination of the ego, to the point that even self preservation was not a concern, is the goal. It is a difficult thing. Our mind is powerful and often does things without our control. How you say? Try this. Close your eyes and think of *nothing* for a whole minute....or ten seconds....can you do it? Probably not. You cannot control your thoughts yet we are admonished to do just that[46]. It is our mind that forms our identity, who we think we are, the "I." It is this 'idea' of ourselves that we seek to protect at all costs; it is not just from physical harm, but from mental hurt and embarrassment. It is the wounded ego that is the cause of most of our problems. It is this we must set aside. The point here is that the setting aside of our ego, with all its ambitions and plans and images and stress and identity, is not a negative thing. It is like the Eastern ideal, specifically within Buddhist tradition of becoming one, eliminating the self and breaking out of the cycle of reincarnation to melt back into the whole. That elimination of identity is disturbing to the Western mind, but Y'shua said that it is only in losing our life that we will find it. The *adam* and his woman found that state in the garden and they were not disappointed in the least.

Finally, they were not disappointed in each other. The search for the suitable helper was over. This reasserts this fact again and they now existed in a state or harmony with their surroundings, fulfilling their duty and experiencing all life had to offer. Things were very good.

---

[46] Matthew 5:19

Genesis 3:1

וְהַנָּחָשׁ הָיָה עָרוּם מִכֹּל חַיַּת הַשָּׂדֶה אֲשֶׁר עָשָׂה יְהוָה
אֱלֹהִים וַיֹּאמֶר אֶל־הָאִשָּׁה אַף כִּי־אָמַר אֱלֹהִים לֹא
תֹאכְלוּ מִכֹּל עֵץ הַגָּן:

And the nechash had been enlightened from out of all the chayah of the field who YHVH the Powers made. And he said to the woman of passion, "Because the Powers said 'you(plural) will not eat from all the trees of the protected place.'"

We are now introduced to a new being in the garden. We will not translate it 'serpent' because that would be too limiting. We don't know what kind of creature it was originally and we will not speculate here on its physical appearance. What we do know is that it was an 'enlightened' being. It had consciousness and the power of communication. According to our verse, that made it unique among all the creatures that YHVH had made in Eden.

The question of motive arises here. Why did the *nechash* seek to deceive the *adam* and his woman? That can be answered by looking at the purpose of the *nechash*. It was created in the garden by YHVH. For what purpose were the *chayah* created in Eden? To see if they would serve as a helper for the *adam*. The *nechash* could very well be the last attempt of YHVH to create a helper that was one of the *chayah*, a very high order of animal with consciousness and speech. It would be king of the *chayah*, the top of the totem pole, yet as a helper it was found wanting. Apparently, the *nechash* also had the capacity to develop ego, because not being picked hurt and engendered a feeling of revenge. It had an axe to grind with the *adam* and its replacement, the woman.

Why did it go after the woman rather than the man? The *nechash* had more experience than her, but not as much as him. Perhaps she is also unaware of its special place in the created order or its history, so she is ignorant of its motives. As the protector of the garden, it would have been the *adam*'s job to remove the *nechash* had he been approached with such a proposal, but by going for the woman, the *nechash* allowed itself time to influence them both.

The *nechash* begins its speech in this verse, but is interrupted by the woman who immediately corrects its statement about the trees. She understands her duty to bring harmony and harmony can only exist where there is truth. She must have thought the *nechash* was looking for a little guidance, seeking some clarification. She may have first felt the spark of ego here, after all, the *nechash* came for such clarification to her and not the *adam*. The *nechash* was driving a wedge between the two that it could exploit and this was just the opening shot. It knew she was well aware of the rules of the place although, as we shall see, she was not quite as sure of the reasons or consequences.

Genesis 3:2

וַתֹּאמֶר הָאִשָּׁה אֶל־הַנָּחָשׁ מִפְּרִי עֵץ־הַגָּן נֹאכֵל:

**But the woman said to the nachash, "From the fruit of the trees
of the protected region we will eat."**

She begins her rhetoric by talking about the command given to her
and the *adam*, they are the 'we.' This probably grated on the *nechash*
because the command was to them, not to it, reminding it of what
could have been. It could also have the unintended consequence of
sparking pride in the woman. The command was given to her and
adam but not any other sentient being. She began to see herself not
only as separate, but perhaps even superior to the other beings in the
created order. This was probably the intent of the *nechash* all along
and it was proving easier than first thought.

Genesis 3:3

וּמִפְּרִי הָעֵץ אֲשֶׁר בְּתוֹךְ־הַגָּן אָמַר אֱלֹהִים לֹא תֹאכְלוּ
מִמֶּנּוּ וְלֹא תִגְּעוּ בּוֹ פֶּן־תְּמֻתוּן׃

"And from the fruit of the trees that are in the middle of the
protected region the Powers said 'you(plural) will not eat from
them and you(plural) will not approach them or you will die.'"

The most obvious thing in this verse is the fact that the woman
expounded on the original command. The 'original command' was not
to eat, but the woman added that the trees in the middle of the
garden were not even to be approached. There could be two causes
for this. First, either the *adam* changed it and made it stronger or the
two of them agreed that neither would even go near it.

What is even more interesting is that she does not differentiate
between the two trees in the middle of the garden. In the center were
not just the trees of the knowledge of function and dysfunction, but
also the trees of life. She says to stay away from them both. But why?
They were not prohibited from eating from the trees of life. Perhaps
this answers our earlier question about where the addition came
from. If the *adam* added to the command, not just about not
approaching the trees of the knowledge of function and dysfunction,
but denying the approach to the center of the garden, perhaps he was
making sure that the 'experiment' with the woman worked out before
they all began eating from the trees of life. It could well be that he had
spent time with the *nechash* after it was created and saw later that it
did not work out and he was giving the woman time to prove that she
was what he thought she was, the perfect helper.

Genesis 3:4

וַיֹּאמֶר הַנָּחָשׁ אֶל־הָאִשָּׁה לֹא־מוֹת תְּמֻתוּן:

And the nechash said to the woman, "No, 'a death will you die.'"

Sensing that the conversation is now becoming based on knowledge, and no one knows everything, the *nechash* corrects the woman. The original commandment found in 2:17 ended with *mot tamot* (a death you will die). In the woman's version in the previous verse, she uses *temutun* (you must die). Either the woman changed what the *adam* told her, or the *adam* changed it for her. The *nechash* now ends its phrase with *mot tamutan* (a death you must die) reinserting the emphasis that was originally given to the *adam*, but using her phraseology. It did this to show that it was more of an expert at what was going on in the garden since it had been around longer that she had. But it didn't want her to feel too left out, so it also included her form to show that she was 'close.' In fact, it was generalizing just as she had. It was a subtle way to set itself up as the teacher, the more knowledgeable one, and putting the woman's experiential focus with its intuition on the back burner. Had she listened to her *neshemah* in this case, she would never have fallen for this, she would have known something was wrong. But the *nechash* put the conversation on a tack that made her the inferior, where in reality; her heightened spiritual state made her the superior.

This is what knowledge does for us; it makes us slaves of the 'experts.' We throw common sense and intuition to the wind and follow the lead of someone who we think knows more than we do. It could be religion, politics, relationships, or science. We don't think we can make a move without an 'expert' telling us what we should do. We don't think we can raise our children without having a library of books. We listen to conflicting reports almost every day as to what we should eat to be healthy. Thirty years ago the experts told us we were heading into an ice age and now its global warming. We put such a premium on knowledge in our culture that the average person feels impotent. That does not need to be the case. If we listen to our *neshemah*, we will know what it is that will bring harmony. The experts may take us down the wrong path and then use more knowledge to try to correct it, which often simply compounds the problem. Solutions are often simple to find, it is the implementation and the sacrifice necessary in lifestyle and attitude that makes them difficult. When the ego is not a factor and the *neshemah* is leading, it becomes much easier.

Genesis 3:5

כִּי יֹדֵעַ אֱלֹהִים כִּי בְּיוֹם אֲכָלְכֶם מִמֶּנּוּ וְנִפְקְחוּ עֵינֵיכֶם
וִהְיִיתֶם כֵּאלֹהִים יֹדְעֵי טוֹב וָרָע:

"For the Powers know for in the day of your(plural) eating from them and your(plural) eyes will be opened and you(plural) will be like the Powers knowing function and dysfunction."

Now that the hook has been swallowed, it is time to set it and reel the woman in. The *nechash* had already sparked her ego by coming to her first instead of the *adam*. It had set itself up as the expert on the rules of the garden, even more so than the *adam*, and had shared a little of that knowledge with her and she had responded favorably. Now it was time to use both those things to get her to do what it wanted.

The *nechash* gives a new definition to the word *mot* (death) by saying that it doesn't mean to die, to cease existing, but that it will open your eyes. In reality, it could be sitting there with her eating from the tree in demonstration since there was no prohibition for it to eat it. It could be showing her the knowledge it had imparted already. It is also telling her that there is a separation between her and the *Elohim*, they are different from her. Not only different but 'better.' Again, a stroke to the ego. The *nechash* was building up an image of separation rather than harmony in her mind. It was making her jealous of the *Elohim*, the same kind of jealousy the *nechash* had for the woman after it had been found inadequate as the helper.

It was all a great sales pitch. The *nechash* didn't really lie to the woman. She didn't die when she touched or ate the fruit. It was true that her eyes were opened. But why did she want it? She had everything in the garden. She, like the *adam*, were superior to the

Elohim by the nature of their created makeup. What the *nechash* was selling her was a step down. In the garden everything was in harmony, it was all *echad*. The *nechash* was introducing separation. But somehow, it made it sound better than it was; it was creating a need where no need existed. In fact, it was leading her down a path that was detrimental. It was surely a salesman who could sell refrigerators to Eskimos. But that is what a knowledge based society is like. Everyone has something to sell, some angle, and it is rarely for the benefit of the recipient. Politicians sell people on courses of action that are socially destructive, yet make us ever more dependent on them. We are sold consumer goods we don't need that just cost us more time and money in the long run. It is all a bill of goods and we are trained from the beginning to accept it. Not just accept it, but to believe that we can't get along without it.

The point of this whole exercise by the *nechash* is to get at the *adam*. It may have been jealous of the woman, but it wanted revenge on the *adam*. So it had to make sure that the woman included him. Now that she had this knowledge, it constantly used the plural 'you' assuming that she would share it with the *adam*. She could now play the expert with it, which would stroke her ego even more, while making her feel good about herself by sharing a wonderful benefit with the one she loved. It's all part of the pitch. She would no longer feel inadequate or like the second fiddle. She would be contributing to the well being of their family group. It played to her ego, as well as her desire to help.

So what really happened when they ate the fruit, what died? It changed their whole perception of reality. It changed their life, from one that was based on experience and intuition, to one based on imperfect knowledge. It took an existence that was in harmony and unity and introduced separation and a dualistic view of all things. It gave them an ego, an illusion that became more of a reality to them than what actually exists, an ego that made them see themselves separate from all things, an ego that could die. It moved the *adam* from a place of partnership with the *Elohim* to antagonist with all the world. This is the world in which we now live.

Genesis 3:6

וַתֵּרֶא הָאִשָּׁה כִּי טוֹב הָעֵץ לְמַאֲכָל וְכִי תַאֲוָה־הוּא
לָעֵינַיִם וְנֶחְמָד הָעֵץ לְהַשְׂכִּיל וַתִּקַּח מִפִּרְיוֹ וַתֹּאכַל וַתִּתֵּן
גַּם־לְאִישָׁהּ עִמָּהּ וַיֹּאכַל׃

**And the woman saw that the function of the tree was for food
and that it was a delight to the eyes and the tree was desirable
for knowledge. And she took from its fruit and she ate and she
gave also to her man with her and he ate.**

The woman now thinks over all that has been said to her by the
nechash. There are three conclusions she comes to. First, the trees of
knowledge of function and dysfunction were now to be regarded as
food whereas before they were not. This is much like the cultural
mores we have regarding what is edible and what is not. The French
may eat snails and frogs and the Chinese may eat what we consider
pets but most Americans don't regard either as food. The *adam* and
the woman may have looked at these trees the same way. Perhaps
after the aforementioned demonstration by the *nechash*, she came to
regard it as edible.

Second, not only was it edible, it now became something desirable to
be eaten, it was a delight to the eyes. The *nechash* has taken
something that was off limits and has turned it into a possibility and
then a desire. The final step of this rationalization was the mental one.
The appetite, a physical longing, had been established. Now she had to
decide mentally if it was good for her. She chose to believe that it was;
it was going to make her a better person, wiser and more
knowledgeable. She had taken the bait, hook line and sinker.

175

But she didn't just reach up and grab the fruit, take a bite and take some to the *adam*. There is a missing conversation between her and the *adam* that takes place between the two sentences. In Genesis 3:17 God says that he 'hearkened unto the voice' of his wife. This conversation, her relating to him all the 'facts' she had learned from the *nechash*, convinced him to join with her in the consumption. She was obviously very persuasive, even making him doubt the command he personally received from God. But what the conversation consisted of is not nearly as important as what happened during it, in fact what has been happening all along.

The *nechash* encouraged the woman to develop her ego, fostering pride and jealousy. Without ego these emotions or feelings cannot exist. She had developed the 'observer self,' a construction of our minds, we identify with the 'I' that watches our life from a vantage point not quite identified with our physical being. It is part of our dualistic perception, a separation of our identity from our actual being. It is an identity that can change as it sees fit. The 'observer self' looks at our being and thinks about what is best and then goes about acquiring it. The 'observer self' is concerned with only one thing, what will make it happy and it will go to any length to procure that or avoid that which will cause pain (emotional) or worst of all, the cessation of its existence.

Think about the animals. They may have some form of emotion, you can tell when your pet dog is happy or sad, but it exists in the moment. It is happy because of some physical circumstance it finds itself in, it is sad because it feels some pain. People, on the other hand, have an 'observer self' that can create these emotions regardless of the circumstances. Not only that, this 'I' can dwell on the past or worry about the future. Animals don't experience that kind of hopelessness and despair. The *adam* and the woman, living in the moment and having their lives based on experience and having eliminated the ego and the 'observer self' had unified their being and were very happy until the *nechash* convinced them they were not as happy as they could be.

Genesis 3:7

וַתִּפָּקַחְנָה עֵינֵי שְׁנֵיהֶם וַיֵּדְעוּ כִּי עֵירֻמִּם הֵם וַיִּתְפְּרוּ
עֲלֵה תְאֵנָה וַיַּעֲשׂוּ לָהֶם חֲגֹרֹת:

**And the eyes of the two of them opened and they knew that
they were enlightened and they sewed fig leaves and they
made themselves aprons.**

They ate the fruit. Was it the fruit itself or is the fruit just an allegory
of the forbidden, a convenient prop for what was really going on
'spiritually'? Isaiah helps us out here by telling us that food does have
an effect on our moral or 'spiritual' makeup. "Butter and honey will he
eat, that he will know to refuse the evil and choose the good[47]." We
cannot separate our 'spiritual' health from our 'physical' health. If we
poison our bodies we poison our spirits as well. Food was a crucial part
of what went on in the garden; God defined what was and was not
food and these commandments were part of the enlightened state of
the garden. One need only look at the many food regulations in the
Torah to understand that what we ingest has an effect on our spiritual
state. Why don't we see it? Because we don't understand it or look for
it. We think that if we eat pork or some chemical laden junk food that
is a delight to the eyes (and tongue) it has no effect on our spiritual
state. It does, but we are so far from enlightenment that it is not
discernable to us. It is like the five hundred pound person that loses
twenty pounds. It is good for him, but it is not discernable. But if a five
foot ten athlete in good shape loses twenty pounds and brings his
body fat to three percent, now one sees the difference between an
individual in good shape and a bodybuilder that can display all his
muscles in sharp definition.

We are so out of tune with spiritual things and the way of the universe that the fine tweaking of diet, while certainly good, does not have the same effect that it did in the garden or among the priests of Israel. This is not to discourage proper diet, just the opposite. It is essential to enlightenment. It is just to say that the effect on us will be less noticeable than among those closer to enlightenment. This is also why fasting is a spiritual exercise. One could say that it is a shortcut of sorts. It cleanses the body of all the trash that has been put into it that hinders connection with the spiritual. Not a fasting that skips a meal or two, but a fasting for days or even weeks. It is hard discipline, but it is discipline that gets us to the garden.

Now that they had eaten the fruit, the 'observer self' could look at their situation and realize that they had been enlightened, but now their situation was different. They have a new way of looking at the world, the way of knowledge.

There are accounts of the first European explorers coming upon 'primitive' tribes in the pacific islands and elsewhere, people whose customs and circumstances and worldview were completely different. They wore little or no clothing. They had no concept of money. In their isolation they assumed this was the normal and correct human condition. Many explorers looked on it as paradise when they first arrived. But their arrival alone changed everything. It revealed to the islanders that there were other options, other ways of living and looking at the world, other value systems. The *nechash* revealed these to the woman and she to the *adam*. They were happy in their bliss and yes, their ignorance. They may have been there long enough that their past outside of the garden was a distant and forgotten memory. The

---

[47] Isaiah 7:15

nechash brought it all back and made a world based on knowledge and ego look like the way to go.

But knowledge is always imperfect. There is no way of knowing all the variables involved in even a simple situation. Therefore, they had now become limited. Whereas before they were unified with the created order and could therefore understand all the variables and their effect and act accordingly; now they had to move within the limits of their own finite intelligence and experience. How did that make them feel? Vulnerable, inadequate and helpless. What is the first thing they did? They made themselves aprons or loincloths, something to cover and protect them from all the things they no longer knew. Before they had been one with the universe, but now everything was largely unknown, even within the garden. It was very scary to them.

There is an additional explanation for the meaning of the phrase "and the eyes of the two of them opened" and it may explain the mystery of what is called the "Cinderella Effect" in physics. Within the creation story we have described the chaotic world of quantum mechanics that underlies our "reality." The "Cinderella Effect" is the term for this contrast between the chaotic world of quantum mechanics and the ordinary, predictable world in which we live. If you think back to the story, Cinderella shows up at the ball in a fancy carriage and dressed beautifully. To those at the ball she was just another person attending the event, beautiful, but ordinary, no different than anyone else. But we know that the underlying reality was that her fairy godmother used magic to bring about the state that others saw as ordinary. The fact is that the quantum world may be explained with some very strange and non-classical physics and the explanation of the facts may lead down some very odd paths, but as far as our everyday reality is concerned, the quantum world hides this "weirdness" and seems unremarkable to us.

The question then becomes, why does nature employ such strange and extraordinary realities in order to keep up ordinary appearances? What if those "ordinary appearances" only exist in our minds as a result of this event? What if the awakening of the ego and its companion, the 'observer self,' altered our perception of reality? It would be like entering "The Matrix," a computer generated world that seems real to us, but in reality only consists of the ones and zeros of computer code.

Consider this. When you sit down to watch television, you enjoy a picture that emanates from the screen. The picture, however, is not real, it is just a construct of your mind, and it is only a result of your limited perception. The reality is that the television screen is made up of thousands of tiny pixels that only show one color at a time and the light that emanates from it comes to your eyes in certain quanta or energy packets, as discussed previously. If you would experience the reality that is what you would see. But we are not in reality. Our mind takes all that information and creates something familiar to us, a picture that corresponds to our past experience. The picture does not exist in the "real world," it only exists in our mind. When we say that our eyes are playing tricks on us, it is not our eyes that are the problem, but the mind being unable to process what we are seeing into something that conforms with our past experiences or worldview.

In Chapter one verse six, we discussed Bell's Theorem and local and non-local reality. If local reality is related to prophesy and true enlightenment then that was what the *adam* had been experiencing in the garden. With the development of the 'observer self' he was now limited to non-local reality. He no longer saw and experienced the universe as a whole, but was limited by time and space. Put these two things together, and the world of the *adam*, at least the world of his perception, had changed radically. In a sense, he created a whole new world. Only this world existed only in his mind. He mistakenly believed this was "enlightenment."

Genesis 3:8

וַיִּשְׁמְעוּ אֶת־קוֹל יְהוָה אֱלֹהִים מִתְהַלֵּךְ בַּגָּן לְרוּחַ הַיּוֹם וַיִּתְחַבֵּא הָאָדָם וְאִשְׁתּוֹ מִפְּנֵי יְהוָה אֱלֹהִים בְּתוֹךְ עֵץ הַגָּן:

And they heard the sound of YHVH the Powers walking in the protected region because of the wind of the work in chaos. And the adam and his woman hid themselves from the face of YHVH the Powers in the middle of the trees of the protected region.

The sound they heard was not the sound of YHVH playing hide and seek. The effect of what the *adam* and the woman had done had reverberated through the garden and the universe. It was a new work in chaos they had begun and it unbalanced everything. All is interconnected and their deed sent ripples out across the ocean of the universe. They were still spiritually sensitive enough to realize this, so they went where they felt safest, back to the scene of the crime, back among the trees that gave them this new outlook. Perhaps they were hoping the trees would give them some insight to deal with the situation as they now found their knowledge wholly inadequate. They could also have sought out the *nechash* to ask it what they should do. They were panicked.

Genesis 3:9

וַיִּקְרָא יְהוָה אֱלֹהִים אֶל־הָאָדָם וַיֹּאמֶר לֹו אַיֶּכָּה:

And YHVH the Powers called to the Adam and said to him, "How?"

YHVH did not need to look for the *adam*. The next verse, in which the conversation begins, presupposes that YHVH has come to him and the *adam* needs to defend his actions. YHVH the powers comes to the *adam*, knowing that something catastrophic has happened in the garden, also knowing what caused it and YHVH asks "How?" It is a question prompted by betrayal. Within that 'how' is a whole history. After I brought you to this place, after I made you ruler and caretaker, after I gave you the woman, after all I have done for you, how could you think of messing it up like this?

The question was not directed at the two of them, but directly to the *adam*. The *adam* was the one in charge, he was the one who received all the instructions, he was the one entrusted with the responsibility to care for the garden therefore, he is the one responsible for wrecking it. It was a very large mess and he was the only one to blame.

Genesis 3:10

וַיֹּאמֶר אֶת־קֹלְךָ שָׁמַעְתִּי בַּגָּן וָאִירָא כִּי־עֵירֹם אָנֹכִי
וָאֵחָבֵא:

And he said, "Your sound I heard in the protected region and I was afraid because I am enlightened and I hid myself."

Now the dance begins. Notice the *adam* does not answer the question of 'how' for to admit his betrayal would make his ego feel bad and it was feeling bad enough. It hurt his pride too much. The unasked question he sees fit to answer is the question of 'why' as in 'why are you hiding.' YHVH had moved past that, he was hiding because he felt guilty, another ego emotion. The hiding is in itself an admission of guilt. Therefore there is no reason to ask the *adam* 'did you do it?' or even 'what did you do?' All that was obvious. But the *adam* was scared, another ego emotion, the sound YHVH made in the garden this time was unfamiliar to him and he tries to stall for time by attempting to redirect the conversation. He was also trying to shift the blame for his behavior to YHVH the powers, 'You scared me.' Not the first shift of blame, as we shall see.

The *adam*, for the first time in our story, says "I." He now has an ego, or at for the first time since coming into the garden. He now bases his interaction with the world on knowledge rather than intuition and wisdom. This has led to fear, guilt, shame, and uncertainty. Without ego, those emotions cannot exist. He knows fear because he now has an ego, an image of himself, that he feels he must protect and he is afraid of losing it or having it injured.

His explanation is an oxymoron. He says "I am enlightened." He equated enlightenment with the knowledge he had gained, he was

185

trying to redefine the terms of the argument. It is all so familiar to us. When faced with guilt, we do anything to justify our wrongdoing. We change the subject, we deny it, we change the meaning of the terms to make what we have done either less severe or actually good. To say "I am enlightened" is an oxy-moron because 'enlightenment' precludes an ego, an 'I.' One cannot have both. To take pride in enlightenment, to boast one has it, merely shows how far one has yet to go. But this is all still so new to the *adam*, he hasn't figured it all out yet.

Genesis 3:11

וַיֹּאמֶר מִי הִגִּיד לְךָ כִּי עֵירֹם אָתָּה הֲמִן־הָעֵץ אֲשֶׁר
צִוִּיתִיךָ לְבִלְתִּי אֲכָל־מִמֶּנּוּ אָכָלְתָּ׃

And he said, "Who proclaimed to you that you were enlightened? The tree species which I commanded you to not eat from, you ate."

YHVH the powers now sounds angry. It is out in the open, the *adam*'s own words had hung him. The accusation was made; the act was exposed and spoken. The truth needs to be spoken before any action; healing, reconciliation or punishment can be brought to bear.

The first thing that needs to be done is to correct the *adam* on his understanding of enlightenment. The *adam* thinks he is enlightened now. The fact was that in his innocent state in the garden he was enlightened, he was living on a whole different plane of existence, he was in touch with all levels of reality. Now he had reduced his understanding considerably, but according to the *nechash*, because he has knowledge, he is enlightened. Knowledge is a good, but only as a basis for existence, relying on this imperfect tool is woefully inadequate, as we see in our world today. It leads to misunderstanding, misguided action, and imperfect understanding of the truth of the world and the divine all because our knowledge is incomplete and always will be. The number of people murdered in the name of God is astounding and it is all because religion is based on knowledge, not truth. The *adam* had exchanged his truth for knowledge and that path is one that leads to death and destruction. One cannot find one's proper place as caretaker of the earth and live in harmony with it if one relies only on knowledge.

The *adam* is no longer enlightened and it is obvious because he took pride in the fact that he thought he was. Enlightenment in not something to be self proclaimed, but recognized by others. Too many charlatans throughout the centuries have proclaimed, "I am the truth" and have duped people for their own ends. Y'shua said it to a few after he had backed it up with action to show that he was enlightened, he was in touch with reality in a way unique in his generation. Moshe showed he was worthy to be followed by his power and humility. The prophets sought nothing but to bring people to the truth. If a leader needs to 'pass the plate' and justify himself, he is no leader.

Genesis 3:12

וַיֹּאמֶר הָאָדָם הָאִשָּׁה אֲשֶׁר נָתַתָּה עִמָּדִי הִוא נָתְנָה־לִּי
מִן־הָעֵץ וָאֹכֵל:

**And the adam said, "The woman who you gave my support,
she gave to me from the trees and I ate."**

The *adam* continues to dig his hole deeper and deeper. No longer can he deny the act, its consequences are obvious to all. The only thing he can think of doing is deflecting responsibility, because he is deathly afraid of the consequences. The guilty verdict has already been proclaimed, he can only seek mitigating circumstances to lessen the punishment, damage control.

We think, at first glance, that he blamed it on the woman. His aim was a little higher. He pointed his finger directly at YHVH, a rather bold move. YHVH took his *tsela* (side) and made the woman. She gave him the fruit, she convinced him as he would never have done it on his own. And on top of that, why were those trees there in the first place? They could have been happy enough without them. It was not the fault of the *adam*, it was the fault of the way YHVH made the garden and the world. "Yes, things are screwed up, but it is the fault of the woman YOU gave me and the garden YOU made!" It is the way a teenager would react. Deny, place blame elsewhere, say the world was against them.

It is all ego, the inability to admit a mistake, to say "I was wrong." The injury to our pride is often too great and we can't take that step so we make it worse. We alienate the ones around us and show ourselves petty and prideful. Perhaps if the *adam* would have admitted it from the start, taken responsibility, showed that he was not ruled by his pride or ego and stood with his wife rather than blame her, things would have been a lot better. He may have even been able to stay. Everyone's path has a few bumps on it. But we will never know because that was not the path he chose.

Genesis 3:13

וַיֹּאמֶר יְהוָה אֱלֹהִים לָאִשָּׁה מַה־זֹּאת עָשִׂית וַתֹּאמֶר
הָאִשָּׁה הַנָּחָשׁ הִשִּׁיאַנִי וָאֹכֵל:

And YHVH the Powers said to the woman, "What is this you did?" And the woman said, "The nechash deceived me and I ate."

The woman finally enters the conversation. She does not just jump in to defend herself even though the *adam* has accused her of being the problem. She waits until YHVH the powers directs the prosecution at her. She puts it squarely on the *nechash*. She was deceived by the *nechash*. The word for 'deceive' is *nasha* and it is the same word used for 'debt.' This may be one of the reasons that interest was not to be charged among the Israelites and that debts were to be cancelled on a regular basis. *Nasha* is a very negative thing.

Why the correlation between deception and debt? When you give someone information to act on, they are placed in your debt. You give them something, information, for 'safekeeping,' they take responsibility for the information. If the information was not correct, the debt is worthless and the actions are at best neutral depending on what the information was used for. If we translate the woman's statement as, "the *nechash* debited me..." you can get a better understanding of the transaction. She had an 'account of truth' to which was added falsehood and therefore the truth was debited from her account.

This goes back to the contrast between a society based on wisdom and one based on knowledge. In wisdom, our 'account of truth' is always growing because it is based on personal experience and

191

intuition, things that are internal to us. We learn and grow and unless we are in the habit of lying to ourselves, our truth account grows. We may not always understand the meaning of our experiences but we know they are true. We may not understand the chemistry of fire or its positive and negative uses, but our experience and intuition tells us we must be careful around it or we will be hurt if we get too close. Because of the nature of wisdom, we cannot debit this account unless we deceive or deny ourselves.

Knowledge, on the other hand, is just the communication of another's experience, intuition or even imagination. If you have no experience with fire and I tell you that if you put your hand in it you will not be injured and you take my word for it, based on your trust in my experience, you will be injured. Or if I tell you that fire is never to be used as it is evil, you would never have the benefit of its warmth or its use for cooking food. With an account based on knowledge, some of it is true, either de facto or based on your experience and some of it is not. We do not know because we are not in their shoes, nor can we be. But we have based our culture on it and therefore our account is constantly in flux, being debited by falsehood or half truth, and credited with facts. The thing is, we never know which is which unless our experience or developed intuition verifies or debunks the information. And when the information comes from a clever one like the *nechash*, who can play with words and disguise the lie with what appears to be truth, and even demonstrate his experience while making it appear to apply to you, it is crucial to be discerning. Even verifiable experience is not always a good guide because what may be good for one is not always good for all. Just because your friend can eat peanuts doesn't mean you, whose experience has taught you that you have a peanut allergy, can eat them. Food for one can be death to another.

Genesis, Zen and Quantum Physics

Now you may say that the command about not eating of the tree is based on accepting the word of YHVH and not on the intuition or experience of the *adam* or the woman. Intuition, however, is understanding the way the world works with all its positive and negative consequences without direct experience. The *adam*, using his intuition, would understand the nature of fire, and while he may not immediately come up with all possible uses, he would have understood its value and danger. Intuition is tapping into the wisdom of the universe which is, of course, God. So while they would not have had direct experience with eating the fruit of the tree, intuitively they would have known it was negative and stayed away from it. By allowing the *nechash* to override their intuition with knowledge, its supposed knowledge, it debited their account of truth.

Our responsibility in giving out information is therefore very heavy. Deceit, either inadvertent or malicious, is always a possibility. That is also why one does not listen to gossip or slander. Such things may go beyond our experience with a person and seek to override our intuition about them and can destroy a relationship very easily. We must guard our truth account carefully and seek to develop our intuition and wisdom and not put so much emphasis on what others are telling us. We should also be very careful with what we tell others and show ourselves trustworthy in our words. Trust is a hard thing to earn and such an easy thing to lose.

Genesis 3:14

וַיֹּאמֶר יְהוָה אֱלֹהִים אֶל־הַנָּחָשׁ כִּי עָשִׂיתָ זֹּאת אָרוּר
אַתָּה מִכָּל־הַבְּהֵמָה וּמִכֹּל חַיַּת הַשָּׂדֶה עַל־גְּחֹנְךָ תֵלֵךְ
וְעָפָר תֹּאכַל כָּל־יְמֵי חַיֶּיךָ׃

**And YHVH the Powers said to the nechash, "Because you did
this, cursed are you from all the walkers and from all the
chayah of the field. On your belly she will walk and the
multitude you will eat all the days of your life."**

The *nechash* is not interrogated by YHVH, it is never given an
opportunity to put up a defense. Why? There are several possibilities.
Was YHVH familiar with his behavior before, was he aware that he
wasn't supposed to be in the garden in the first place and the *adam*
neglected his guard duty where it was concerned? Did the *nechash*
have a reputation already? Had YHVH been watching the whole
conversation and act? If this is the case it would not only have been to
see if the two of them would fall for the lie, move into the realm of
knowledge, but also to see what their reaction would be when
confronted. Certainly their act of eating from the tree was
disappointing in itself, but to see the way the *adam* reacted with such
a lack of maturity must have been devastating. To see someone who
had reached the highest level of enlightenment fall so quickly and
completely was just horrifying.

The word for 'curse' is *arar* which means to spit on something, to hold
it in utter contempt. The *nechash* had wanted all along to be
separated out from among the other *chayah* so he could be the
adam's helper. Now it got its wish to be separated out. One of the
reasons we did not translate 'neshash' as serpent was because in this

verse and the next it is not necessary to associate the *nechash* with snakes. Snakes are part of the ecosystem, and a beneficial one, I might add. But there is also a very long history of associating the *nechash* with either snakes or other reptiles such as dragons. There are several ancient mythologies that refer to a serpent/dragon being killed to make the world. If we take our translation at face value it means exactly what it says. The woman will walk on the belly[48] of the *nechash*. The *nechash* will support her footsteps on her journey through life. The *nechash* could literally be the earth itself. Because of the debt previously discussed, it is now responsible for her. This is referring to the worldview she has now accepted, a worldview based on knowledge. She wanted it, now she has it. The *nechash* gave it to her and it is now responsible for her. Both *Ish* (man) and *Isha* (woman) are now 'grounded' from their previous spiritual heights.

The second half of the 'curse' is that the *nechash* will 'eat the multitude.' The Hebrew *aphar*, which is usually translated as 'dust' just means a lot of something, a multitude. What is the multitude it will eat? The descendants of the woman. She has brought about the less than perfect conditions in the world, there is no longer harmony. Death will now stalk them and when it overcomes them, they will return to the earth-dust to dust. The *nechash* will literally eat the multitude of their descendants.

---

[48] The Hebrew word *telekh* can be translated as 'you will walk' or 'she will walk.'

Genesis 3:15

וְאֵיבָה אָשִׁית בֵּינְךָ וּבֵין הָאִשָּׁה וּבֵין זַרְעֲךָ וּבֵין זַרְעָהּ
הוּא יְשׁוּפְךָ רֹאשׁ וְאַתָּה תְּשׁוּפֶנּוּ עָקֵב: ס

"And enmity I will make between you and the woman, and between your seed and her seed. He will strike you, the head, and you will strike us, the heel."

This is probably one of the most well known and interpreted verses in Genesis, perhaps the Bible as a whole. It is understood as messianic by many, Christian and Jew. Let's take a new look at it and try to figure out exactly what is being talked about here.

The 'seed' in the verse, in both instances, is singular. There is a seed of the woman and the seed of the *nechash*. What is the 'seed' of the *nechash*? Is it a people group? Is it a person like the 'anti-christ'? Is the seed of the woman the messiah? In the last verse, we stated that the *nechash* had become the worldview of knowledge that now supported the woman and that, we propose, is the seed of the *nechash*. That would mean that her seed would be the opposite, a worldview based on wisdom. It would seem fitting as well, knowing that women, much more so than men, are known for their intuition. What we have is a conflict between two worldviews that has always been a part of history. It is just like the tension created between order and chaos; it is something built into the fabric of the universe. This is not so much a curse on the *nechash,* but a recognition of the consequences of its behavior of the *adam* and the woman. What has changed for the *adam* and the woman is that their short sojourn in 'utopia,' where the impact of one worldview (knowledge) was minimized, is over. It would seem that the only way to achieve utopia, as we mentioned before, is

196

to be alone with no temptation to sin against another, no reason to develop ego with no one to impress. The *Torah* as a body of laws and regulations exists to mold a community in such a way as to minimize the egos of the people involved. It applies equally to all, its specific laws are designed to punish those who develop ego and act on it, even the idea of hereditary position work to eliminate ego. There is no rational basis for ego in a genetic lottery. One cannot do anything to be the firstborn or to be a priest or member of some other tribe, so how can one take pride in such a position? One only needs to fulfill the unearned responsibility. That is why God was so opposed to a king. Saul was chosen in a way that stroked his ego, tall and handsome, a warrior type. David was the opposite, but even he let ego destroy what could have been a great reign. Solomon and his sons made it even worse by modeling themselves after the ego rich oriental kings around them. The *nechash* was winning most of the rounds here.

Let us define the rest of our terms now. The 'he' is the seed of the woman; the 'head' is the *nechash;* the 'heel' and the 'us'[49] are YHVH *Elohim.* By placing the *nechash* at the head and YHVH *Elohim* at the heel, it reverses the natural order of things. It is by its very nature, disharmonious. By choosing the way of knowledge, man has put the *nechash,* and its worldview, as the head. The truth and wisdom has become the hind part, the heel, for it will always be a struggling minority. Y'shua taught many a time that the way is hard and few find it. But there will always be enmity between the two, there will always be conflict. Ultimately, if man will be honest with himself and seek the truth, he will find the way of knowledge wholly unsatisfying and the way of wisdom will cry out for him.

---

[49] The Hebrew word *teshuphenu* can be translated as "you will strike him" or "you will strike us."

Man will constantly seek to break the yoke placed on him by the *nechash* for we were not created to be subject to it. What is this yoke? Y'shua again taught that his yoke was easy and his burden light which implies there is a harder yoke. He was contrasting the way of wisdom and the way of knowledge, the yoke of the *nechash* and the yoke of YHVH. The yoke of YHVH is the way of the garden, the way of enlightenment, the way of wisdom and intuition, the way of harmony. The yoke of the *nechash* is the way of knowledge. What is the first thing man desires to know? First God and then himself. However, seeking God through knowledge is a dead end street, it leads nowhere. We cannot analyze God scientifically, God cannot be quantified.

So what are we left with? The same thing the *nechash* gave eve: supposition, conjecture, imagination, and hypothesis. Where does this lead? Religion. One man or a group of men, with egos to boot, come up with a 'picture' of God that can be related to through knowledge. They make God in their own image. God is personified and as such, we can refer to this God as the "Man on the Throne." You know the picture: older guy, long white beard, scepter, light around the head. He exists to dictate rules, hear petitions (prayer) and judge behavior. He demands obedience and his representatives, the priests, are there to interpret and enforce his will.

This results in several things. The idea of exclusivity, "I know God and you don't, you are therefore different from me, and you need to convert to my way of thinking." It results in a religious cult run by a few select people who reserve the right of interpretation, rule making and judgment to themselves. Those same select few will seek to take the production and wealth of others for themselves in the name of their God. This emphasis leads to a consumer mentality in which production and accumulation are seen as good, a result of being close to God. After all, the priests who are closest to God are wealthy and they must be blessed, so if I become wealthy that means I am blessed. It inflates the ego and creates disparity between people, 'the have' and 'the have nots.' This all leads to a misallocation of resources and waste, which creates disharmony in the world, a disharmony that needs to be corrected at some point, usually catastrophically. This is exactly the wish of the *nechash*.

But it also leads to confusion and uncertainty for the individual. If one desires to please God, there will never be a lack of people who will gladly tell one how to do so. The question becomes, which one is right? Is it the cult of Isis, or the Oracle of Delphi, or a mystery cult? Is it Roman Catholic, Methodist, Baptist, Fundamentalism or Latter Day Saints? Is it Reform, Conservative or Orthodox Judaism? Is it Wahabism, Sunni or Shi'ite. Is it Bhuddism, Hinduism, Shintoism or Taoism? You get the idea. Even when you pick your religion (or you believe your religion picked you), there are still a multitude of choices. So, one needs to pick a subgroup or person to follow. Did one pick the right one? How does one know? Even if one is comfortable with the choice, how does one know one is doing enough? Does one know all the rules and rituals and is one performing them correctly? If one can't be perfect, how much is enough? Is the leader or group going to come up with a new revelation that will expose some ignorance on everyone's part and what will the result be? Can one rely on the mercy of God to overlook one's feeble attempt at correct behavior and how far does that mercy extend? If God is all merciful, does one have to take this so seriously at all? Is it law or faith, judgment or mercy and if it is a combination, at what point does the balance tip? How does one know God is hearing one's prayers and can anything be done to motivate him to answer as one desires? If we are honest with ourselves about our religion these questions will arise. Of course the priest, minister, rabbi or imam or whatever, will have an answer for us, he or she will seem sure, they will teach us the traditions that will continue their power, they may even threaten us with hell or excommunication if we doubt their word.

These are the reasons the prophets and Y'shua were persecuted and distrusted by the powerful elite, but loved by the people. Y'shua pointed out that the rabbis, or even the priests, did not have the exclusive rights to the way of God, any man could find it. But it was not just this egalitarian approach that made trouble. He also made direct attacks on the idea that wealth and position were blessings, that the religious cult and the consumer mentality were essential parts of the way of God and one need only 'fine tune' the rules and regulations around it to 'find God' or 'please God.' He chose not to participate in their theological arguments about heaven or hell or rules, for this was all based on the way of the *nechash*, the way of knowledge. He told people to drop out of the system, take up a cross and follow his example. When the rich came seeking the way, he told them to give it up, their wealth was holding them back. "It is harder for a rich man to find the kingdom than a camel to go through the eye of a needle[50]." Why? Because as he taught in the parable of the seeds, the cares of the world will choke a young plant and kill it.

This is why so few people in Western countries find true spirituality. They don't have the time for the discipline and the community essential for the journey. It is the simple life, the life of a nomad that he impressed on his followers and while that life and mentality existed, the teachings and community founded by Y'shua flourished and grew and demonstrated great spiritual power. When men with egos began seeking position and Rome ascended in the second century, the spiritual power ebbed and temporal power took over and

---

[50] Matthew 19:24

it became what it is today, just another religion based on imperfect knowledge.

But the way is still there, there are still those who find the narrow path. Many of the teachings of Y'shua and the prophets are still with us. The conflict still exists and if we do not bury it beneath our hectic lives spent chasing more stuff, the enmity between the way of the *nechash* and the way of YHVH *Elohim* will surface and we will have a real choice. Will we feed our ego thinking that if we just find the right set of rules to follow we will please the 'man on the throne' and be blessed or get into heaven? Or will we suppress ego, drop out of consumer society and seek the path of wisdom where the real experience of the divine awaits?

Genesis 3:16

אֶל־הָאִשָּׁה אָמַר הַרְבָּה אַרְבֶּה עִצְּבוֹנֵךְ וְהֵרֹנֵךְ בְּעֶצֶב
תֵּלְדִי בָנִים וְאֶל־אִישֵׁךְ תְּשׁוּקָתֵךְ וְהוּא יִמְשָׁל־בָּךְ׃ ס

To the woman he says, "I will greatly increase the your labor and your pregnancy, in pain you will bear children and to your man is your desire and he will rule in you."

There are two interesting parts of this verse as YHVH *Elohim* dictates the consequences for the woman. The first is in the area of childbearing. In the natural order of things, giving birth is easy unless there is some abnormality. Animals give birth or lay eggs and there is little, if any, pain or difficulty. Some animals, like bears and other hibernators, give birth and don't even wake up! That is not true for woman and also for other animals that we have decided to bring into our circle of pain through domestication. Women get morning sickness, they get moody, their hormones become erratic and then there is labor and delivery. Even when not pregnant, there is PMS and afterwards, post partum depression. This behavior, both physiological and psychological, is unique to our species. It is a result of the disharmony we have created ever since the fall. And we have spread some of it to our domesticated animals which is why, on a farm, cows and horses and the like often need our help, while in the wild, they get along quite well without us. In the process of domestication, we introduce unnatural environments and behaviors to them and these difficulties are the result.

The second part has to do with the relationship that will now exist between a man and a woman. First, after telling her that childbirth will be a miserable experience, the woman may just decide not to have any. That was not going to happen, for her desire was to be for her husband. There would be something within her psyche that would make her want to have a family. We jokingly refer to this as a woman's 'biological clock,' but the desire of women to have children is a strong one in most. So her 'nesting instinct' will overpower her aversion to pain (or even fear of death) so much so that she will often have more than one child.

This verse also creates a hierarchy where one did not exist before. The man is to 'rule in her.' This was codified in many cultures, including that of the Israelites. A woman was under the authority of her father and then her husband. It is a recognition of the new state of things for in a world based on knowledge, hierarchies are a natural result because knowledge is, by its very nature, distributed unequally. Some will always accumulate more knowledge and authority than others. YHVH was telling the woman that the man would be in this position. He had shown himself to be filled with ego through his conversation and YHVH was telling the woman that in this new order they had created, the man would have the ego and the emphasis on knowledge, while she would maintain more intuition and wisdom. It wasn't how things were supposed to be and it would put mankind at a real disadvantage in returning to the garden. The leadership, man, would have a natural tendency away from wisdom while those that had more wisdom would be placed in a subservient position. But again, there would be tension, for this is not the natural order of things and women would not be altogether comfortable in this position. Women have sought to reestablish their original position in a variety of ways, more recently by becoming like men and seeking the same power. By building up their egos, such women are denying their true power. The conflict will remain between men and women because of the disharmony of this present order and it is only when the original cooperation is reestablished by lack of ego on both sides that harmony will result.

Genesis 3:17

וּלְאָדָם אָמַר כִּי־שָׁמַעְתָּ לְקוֹל אִשְׁתֶּךָ וַתֹּאכַל מִן־הָעֵץ
אֲשֶׁר צִוִּיתִיךָ לֵאמֹר לֹא תֹאכַל מִמֶּנּוּ אֲרוּרָה הָאֲדָמָה
בַּעֲבוּרֶךָ בְּעִצָּבוֹן תֹּאכְלֶנָּה כֹּל יְמֵי חַיֶּיךָ:

**And to Adam he said, "Because you listened to the voice of
your woman and you ate from the tree which I commanded
you saying, 'you will not eat from him,' the ground is cursed in
your production. In pain you will eat of her all the days of
your life."**

Adam has now become a proper name. It is no longer a generic
designation; 'the *adam*,' but it is now 'Adam.' This goes along with his
new found ego. He now prepares for the consequences of his actions.
But before they are given, YHVH *Elohim* wants to make a few things
clear. First of all, he says, "you listened," declaring Adam at fault. He
had a choice to listen to God or the woman and he chose to listen to
the woman. Second, it was not to 'the woman' that God gave him, but
'your woman.' Adam had tried to shift the blame on YHVH by saying
that if he had not had the woman given to him, he would not have
done this thing. YHVH corrects him; she is 'his woman.' She was made
from him and he was very happy with her when she showed up. He
can't discount or disown her now. They are in this together and he is
responsible for her as well as his own actions. He was to guard the
garden and he did not do his duty and he should have kept her from
listening to the *nechash* in the first place. Finally, YHVH reminded him
of the command. He was not to eat from those trees, he received the
command, it was clear, and there should have been no doubt. He was
guilty of willful disobedience.

In the garden sustenance was easy. Food and water was easily obtainable, it was a hunter/gatherer paradise. Even the planting and tending of things was easy. Everything was in harmony: soil, air and water, so providing for their basic needs was easy. Not anymore. Now the earth itself was cursed and it would not easily yield to the work of man. But this is not just the hard work necessary to plant crops, trying to get a sustainable yield in less than perfect conditions. The pain is not just the physical labor necessary; it is the production necessary to feed the ego that will also cause pain. The hunter/gatherer knows no hard work under ideal conditions. Every day he simply gathers what he needs just like the 'birds of the air,' as Y'shua put it. There is no lack, there is no extra. It was just like gathering the manna in the desert. Each one, whether they gathered a lot or a little had enough and no more. There was no pride in accumulation. There was no waste.

With ego comes pride and fear. It is pride in having more than your neighbor. It is fear that it could be taken away, that there will not be enough tomorrow. Some of the Israelites needed to learn that in the desert, they tried to keep some of the manna for the next day and it grew maggots and stank. They were relying on their knowledge, which was lacking in this case. They had little experience with manna, so they didn't know if it would be there tomorrow. One using wisdom and intuition, being connected with the harmonious nature of the universe, would have understood that the manna would keep coming and there was nothing to worry about. But Adam had chosen the way of knowledge so he, and we, will spend our lives in toil, trying to accumulate more and more, afraid that there will never be enough until we die, surrounded by our accumulated stuff. It is so sad to see people, who spend their lives working so hard, consuming and accumulating so much, at the expense of the most important things in life, and then die without realizing how much they have wasted away over the years.

Genesis 3:18

וְקוֹץ וְדַרְדַּר תַּצְמִיחַ לָךְ וְאָכַלְתָּ אֶת־עֵשֶׂב הַשָּׂדֶה:

"And she(the ground) will cause brambles and weeds to grow for you and you will eat the green plants of the field."

The most obvious meaning of this verse is that not only would the work of sustenance be difficult, as the next verse points out, but that the earth itself would conspire against Adam and bring forth things that are not edible or helpful. In the garden everything was separate and functional. The story of Genesis chapter one was one of separation, making things functional as individual parts of the whole, the unity of the created order. In Eden, that which was edible and helpful for Adam was separate and easily accessible and differentiated from that which was not useful to him. Now, things would return to the state before the separation. The weeds and edible plants will now grow together, that which is functional and that which is not are mixed and Adam will have to work to separate them.

There are two parables that come to mind when we consider weeds. The first is found in Matthew 13:24-30 where Y'shua tells his audience that the Kingdom of Heaven is like a man who sowed good seed in his field and then an enemy sowed bad seed. The man decided to let the good (the wheat) and bad (the tares) grow up together until the harvest when the bad would be taken out and burned and the good put in the storehouse. If we put this parable together with what has been happening in this chapter of Genesis, we find that the kingdom exists here and now, if we are only able to discern it from the "tares." Adam had experienced the "Kingdom" easily and in all its glory in the garden, now he would have to search for it, a point Y'shua made repeatedly.

207

The other is found in Matthew 13:3-23, it is the parable of the sower. A sower sows his seed and some of it falls on the path, some of it on the rocks, some of it grew up and was choked by weeds and finally, some fell on good soil and grew up to be productive. For our purposes we will concentrate on the plants choked by the weeds. The weeds are dysfunctional; literally the word refers to plants that are attractive but useless. In the garden, the Adam was surrounded by good soil. Now he is literally surrounded by thorns and weeds. The weeds will grow "for" (literally toward) the Adam, they will surround him and seek to choke the life out of him. In the garden the chaos was held at bay, now it is aggressively seeking to envelope him. In Y'shua's parable, the weeds are representative of the worries of life and the wealth of the world that chokes the young plant. How does this relate to our narrative in Genesis? The words we translated as "bramble" and "weeds" could also be translated as "fear" and to "circle in flight." The meaning of the verse would then be that Adam would eat in fear. Where does the fear come from, the fear of loss, fear of deprivation, fear of not having enough to sustain himself and the fear that what he has will be taken away? It all stems from the ego. This is exactly what Y'shua was talking about. There was no fear and no need in the garden. Outside the garden, fear was everywhere and until we heed Y'shua's warning and learn to be in harmony with the world around us and live like the flowers of the field and the birds of the air, fear and worry will rule our lives. This verse tells Adam what his life is now going to be like. Not a pretty picture to be sure and I am sure Adam would want to make his way back to his previous state.

The only other place in the Bible that uses the phrase 'brambles and weeds' is in Hosea 10:8 where the prophet says that brambles and weeds would grow over the alter of God. The alter represents the way to commune with the Creator and the brambles and weeds would hide it. For Adam, and us, the way of God is hidden by the ego and the cares and worries of the world as well as the desire to accumulate wealth and knowledge that come with that ego. It is only by following the way of God as outlined in the *Torah*[51] that our fields will be productive once again and we will have a chance of finding the Kingdom of God.

The question arose in our study of this verse as to why this verse includes, "you will eat the green plants of the field." Why was this command given again? Adam had already been instructed about his diet, why remind him here? The reason is because Adam needed to be told that although his circumstances were about to change radically, the rules had not. We have mentioned before that in the Hebrew mindset, there is no division between the "spiritual" and the "physical." Just as there are physical laws like gravity that do not change and remain no matter what, there are moral and spiritual laws that do not change. Perhaps, expelled from the garden, Adam would think that there must be different rules for new circumstances. The fact is, basic morality does not change regardless of circumstances. We would do well to remember this admonition as we so often hear, in these modern times, morality must change. Ignoring the basic rules of the universe, physical or moral, will have disastrous consequences. It leads to imbalance and that leads to catastrophic realignment, just as the people of Sodom and Gomorrah discovered.

---

[51] Specifically Deuteronomy 28

Genesis 3:19

בְּזֵעַת אַפֶּיךָ תֹּאכַל לֶחֶם עַד שׁוּבְךָ אֶל־הָאֲדָמָה כִּי מִמֶּנָּה לֻקָּחְתָּ כִּי־עָפָר אַתָּה וְאֶל־עָפָר תָּשׁוּב:

"With the sweat of your nostrils you will eat bread again. You returned to Ha'adamah given that from her you were taken, given that a multitude are you and to the multitude you will return."

The first thing we notice about this verse is that it is a continuation, or parallel, of the ideas in the previous verse. The 'sweat' referred to here is not the simple sweat of a hard day's work, but the sweat that comes from being afraid, or more precisely, terrified. The word 'bread' in this verse comes from a root meaning 'fighting,' probably in reference to the kneading process where the bread is beaten and manhandled. So the first part of the verse contains the idea that Adam is going to be terrified as he fights for his sustenance. He will have to work hard, yes, but he will always be fearful that his work will not be successful, that the earth will not yield its produce.

We have consistently translated *Adamah* as a place name and postulated that this is where Adam was originally "pressed out" from. We have translated the Hebrew *ad* as 'again' and the "again" here reinforces the idea that he is returning to a way of life and the people he was very familiar with and had left. This may give us another insight into what the source of his fear or "terror" was. As Y'shua said, a prophet is respected everywhere, but his hometown[52]. In the ancient world, loyalty to one's clan or tribal group was paramount. For Adam to leave of his own accord, because he found them deficient, would

---

[52] Mark 6:4

have been a grave insult. Look at what happened to Lot in Sodom. He tried pointing out their faults, he "judged" them[53], and they tried to kill him. Adam could expect little better upon his return.

This idea of returning to his place is reiterated in the second half of the verse, "to the multitude you will return." In Genesis 2:7 he was pressed out of the multitude of *Adamah* and now he is returning. What does it mean, however, for Adam himself to be a "multitude"? A multitude is a group of things and is the opposite of one thing, something that is *"echad."* In the garden, Adam was a unity of *Ayn Soph* and the powers, of "mind and womb[54]." He existed in the garden with a singular mind and purpose in harmony with all things. Upon partaking of the tree of knowledge, however, he had become splintered. He now had an 'observer self' and an ego. Within him there was no longer harmony. Think of your own experience. When you wrestle with a difficult decision, are there not separate parts of you that argue with one another, different aspects of your person that look at things and react to them in different ways? In the garden Adam did not have this experience, he always knew the correct decision because he was tapped into the very fabric of the universe, he experienced "local" reality. The course of action was always clear because he operated in wisdom. Now, working with imperfect knowledge, there were gaps in his understanding, which created hesitation and opened up possibilities that were not there before.

Finally, this is a recognition of the choice he had made to listen to the *nechash*. In Genesis 3:14 it is stated that the *nechash* will eat the "multitude." The way of life and the Kingdom of God were open to him, but now he will go the way of all things and be devoured in the

---

[53] Genesis 19:9

[54] See our Quantum Translation of Genesis 1:27

end. He had chosen to serve the *nechash* and he would now become consumed by it.

Genesis 3:20

וַיִּקְרָא הָאָדָם שֵׁם אִשְׁתּוֹ חַוָּה כִּי הִוא הָיְתָה אֵם כָּל־חָי:

**And Adam met the character of his woman. He declared that
she was the mother of all the living ones.**

The first thing we may notice is that this verse is not simply the
'naming' of Adam's wife or a recognition of the fact that she was the
'first mother.' The word *chavah*, which is usually written as the name
'Eve,' means 'to declare' and really has nothing to do with the second
half of the verse if it is meant to be a name. In the Scriptures, the
naming of someone is usually preceded by an event or followed by an
explanation related to the name. That is not the case here, so for this
reason, we have translated this verb as "to declare."

The second half of the verse states that "she was the mother of all the
living ones" and the verb *haytah* is in the perfect tense which denotes
completed action, she 'was' the mother of all the living ones. There is
a problem with this, however. This means her reproduction would
have happened in the past. There are two possible explanations for
this. The first is that this is an editorial statement of fact added at a
later time. This would seem obvious except for the fact that we have
consistently asserted that 'Adam and Eve' were not the first or only
people on earth and there were other 'mothers' on the earth.
Therefore, as an editorial statement taken at face value, it would be
false.

The second possibility is that Adam and 'Eve' had had children in the
garden. There is nothing to disprove this as the amount of time they
spent there is never specified. In Genesis 2:20 we translated *kara* as

'met'[55] and we continue that here in this verse, and another meeting happens here as well. The question is, why? Because of the new circumstances they find themselves in and how they are going to deal with it in relation to the children.

What is going on here is that YHVH has told Adam what is going to happen, life was going to become very difficult for him. After hearing this, Adam asserts two things with his statement. First, he makes a declaration concerning his wife which demonstrates his authority over her, an authority given to him by YHVH in Genesis 3:16. The second, by recalling the 'meeting' with the 'characters' of the animals, he is attempting to reassert his role in the garden prior to 'the fall.' He accepts his punishment and has begun the process of rehabilitating himself by starting to take responsibility for himself and his wife again, something he had discarded in the previous 'blame game.' Even though YHVH was the one that had been doing the accusing, Adam understands that he shares an essential nature with YHVH and although he has failed, he still has that nature in the same way that he was still expected to follow the rules. Therefore, he says to YHVH that his woman was the mother of all the children that they had in the garden and the implication is that he is interceding for them. He and his woman will bear the brunt of the consequences, but he asks that the children be taken into consideration. Apparently, based on the following verses, he was given a reprieve and at least for a time allowed to stay in the garden.

The question naturally arises, what happened to these children and, by extension, Eden? Chapter four makes it clear that they probably did

---

[55] The Hebrew verb *kara* means "to call out to meet with" and can mean to "call," "call out" or "meet."

not exit the garden with their parents. Therefore, they must not have partaken in their parents "fall" and remained in paradise.

There is a lot of speculation as to where the Garden of Eden was/is located. We would propose that the garden was a real place and exists today, but does so either in another dimension or in a parallel/alternate universe. Certainly physics supports the idea of multiple universes, perhaps even an infinite number. These universes can be connected in a variety of ways, including wormholes. We have speculated that Moshe had the opportunity to enter the garden at the burning bush and that Enoch, Elijah and Y'shua found the way in. It could very well be that the garden is populated by such men (and women) from our world but also by the children of Adam and even others who have found Eden/paradise/The Kingdom of God. So where is it? Y'shua said that it was "near at hand," in fact that it "is within you." Another dimension/universe can be anywhere; we only need eyes to see.

Genesis 3:21

וַיַּעַשׂ יְהוָה אֱלֹהִים לְאָדָם וּלְאִשְׁתּוֹ כָּתְנוֹת עוֹר וַיַּלְבִּשֵׁם:

**YHVH of the Powers made for the adam and his woman
coverings of skin and he clothed them.**

This is the second set of clothes for the Adam and his woman. Clothing in the context of the garden is a very interesting thing. The purpose of clothing in general is for protection, commonly from the elements. The fact that YHVH made clothing for them is a demonstration of his care and concern for them even in the face of his disappointment. It is also the first reference to the killing of an animal; we could call it the "first sacrifice." The purpose of this sacrifice, however, is very mundane; it is for physical protection, for the garden has now become a more dangerous place. How so? Most obviously, the thorns would now be intermixed with the plants he used for food. That was not all they needed protection from, however. The *nechash* was still lurking about and he had been condemned without a defense and he could be looking to further harm Adam and his woman. Their disobedience also introduced more chaos into the garden, throwing it out of balance. They also needed protection from the very presence of YHVH himself. Just as Moshe was not permitted to experience the full 'glory' of YHVH, Adam had lost that privilege as well.

There is a difference in this set of clothes, however. In Genesis 3:7, they fashioned themselves clothes out of fig leaves. It was an attempt to continue what they had begun by eating the fruit, which many traditions state was a fig. By making clothes for themselves, they were continuing to create an image of themselves that would be acceptable to their 'observer self,' their ego. In fact, clothes represent the veil that now separates us from God, from reality, just as idolatry divorces us from the reality of God by creating a false and inadequate impression. Clothing reinforces the illusion our ego creates and becomes a source of pride. It is also interesting to note that the Hebrew word for a 'fig' is in fact related to the word for 'I,' the ego, both words coming from the root אן (ahn).

In this verse, YHVH makes the clothes. Clothes are now necessary, but the clothes they had fashioned were totally inadequate. It was previously mentioned that the clothes were for protection, but it is more than that. Garments are related to armor, which while primarily defensive, is meant to protect the wearer in battle. In the garden the battle may be with the elements, but he also needed to be clothed with the armor provided by YHVH to get back to the garden after he was removed. We need to put off the garments we make for ourselves in the mistaken pursuit of ego and put on the garments provided us by YHVH as we journey toward Eden. We never know when we may need the garments. Revelation 16:15 says that we need to stay awake and keep our clothes with us. The trials and refining fires that lead to Eden can come at any time during our journey. Preparation and vigilance are the keys.

Genesis 3:22

וַיֹּאמֶר יְהוָה אֱלֹהִים הֵן הָאָדָם הָיָה כְּאַחַד מִמֶּנּוּ לָדַעַת
טוֹב וָרָע וְעַתָּה פֶּן־יִשְׁלַח יָדוֹ וְלָקַח גַּם מֵעֵץ הַחַיִּים
וְאָכַל וָחַי לְעֹלָם׃

**And YHVH the Powers said, "Look the man is like a unity
apart from us knowing function and dysfunction and now
turning, will send his hand and will take also from the trees of
the chayim and will eat and live forever."**

The first part of this verse summarizes the changes that have taken
place. While most translations have "the man has become like one of
us," it ignores the Hebrew word *mimenu* meaning 'from us.' The man
did not 'become like God' as a result from the fall, he was already that
prior to the fall. This passage is stating that he is now 'apart from' God.

As we have previously stated, the goal is to return to the garden, or to
put it another way, to enter into the kingdom of God and to once
again be *echad* with, or to be a part of, *Elohim*. Moshe achieved this
after his 'burning bush' experience when YHVH told him, "I have made
you *Elohim*[56]." We also know that Y'shua had achieved this when he
said, "I and the Father are one[57]."

What has changed for Adam is his relation to the *Elohim* and the rest
of the created order. He is now "like a unity." He was created to be the
unifying force of creation; he was made in the shadow of *Ayn Soph*. He
was at the top of the created order. Now he is just a pale imitation of
what he once was. He resembled the unity of all creation, but by

---

[56] Exodus 7:1
[57] John 10:30

218

separating himself from everything else, he denied himself the power and experience of that unity.

"Knowing function and dysfunction" are just labels we assign to things through our ego and 'observer self' based on how they affect us. In a balanced world, everything is functional and in balance. If we are in tune to those things and have no fear or worry, we will not experience dysfunction. It is only when we look at the natural world as equipment to be utilized to fulfill the needs of our ego that things in the world become good and evil. Only in a world in which we find our value in the things we have accumulated do the natural processes of the earth take on negative connotations. The river floods and destroys my house and the things I have in it, therefore the flood is "bad." The natural world is not good or bad, it just is. It is only our reaction to it that can be functional or dysfunctional and the more we try to control it, manipulate it or conquer it; the more dysfunctional it will appear to us. Adam was once in harmony with the natural world. Now he was creating an image of dissention and he would soon find out just how bad that could be.

The second half of the verse describes the course of action that needs to be taken. He is now separate and out of balance with the created order. He is no longer *echad* with YHWH, *Ayn Soph*, or the world around him. What if he takes fruit from the trees of life and lives forever in this state? There are two problems with allowing Adam eternal life at this point. The first is that he could have kept introducing more and more chaos into the garden indefinitely. This would have brought untold misery to all of creation. The second is that by introducing (or reintroducing) death to Adam, God offers a very powerful motivator for change. If Adam was allowed to live forever in the garden, in a sense never suffering the consequences of his separation, he would have had no motivation for seeking reunification. But if everlasting life is a goal rather than a fact, Adam and all who come after him have something to work towards. We can seek eternal life by seeking the reunification that results from eliminating the ego, becoming children again and seeing the *echad* of all things. Y'shua said the Kingdom of God is within each of us and that is true because the fundamental order of the universe has not changed, only our perception of it. We can experience it just as Adam did if we look within, eliminate the ego and open ourselves up to the reality of the world around us.

Genesis 3:23

וַיְשַׁלְּחֵהוּ יְהוָה אֱלֹהִים מִגַּן־עֵדֶן לַעֲבֹד אֶת־הָאֲדָמָה
אֲשֶׁר לֻקַּח מִשָּׁם:

**And YHVH of the Powers sent him from the protected region
in Eden to serve Ha'adamah, which is where he was taken
from.**

This verse provides another proof of the authors' contention that
Adam was not created in the garden but came from the outside, a
region/city called *Ha'adamah* from which his name was derived. The
verse itself is self explanatory. YHVH is sending Adam back to
Ha'adamah to serve it, or the people thereof. The word usually
translated as 'till' or 'work' is the Hebrew word *avod*, which means to
serve and when used in relation to God is often translated as
'worship.' The word 'send' is the Hebrew *shalach* which in its noun
form can be translated as 'apostle.' If we put all this together, we have
the idea that Adam was sent back to *Ha'adamah* as an ambassador or
a prophet. In fact, the idea of 'sending' someone is used specifically in
this way in Judges 6:8 and II Samuel 12:25.

The question naturally arises, why? The most obvious is that Adam is
returning to share his experience, wisdom and knowledge with the
people of *Ha'adamah*. This would be one of the traditional roles of a
prophet or ambassador of YHVH. Beyond that there is the idea in the
New Testament that Y'shua is the "second Adam," that he fulfills the
role in which the first Adam failed to fulfill. However, this may have
more to do with Adam's spiritual development than that of the people
of *Ha'adamah*.

We have asserted that Adam's life was a journey that had led him to the garden. We make a mistake in assuming, however, that the garden is the end of the journey. The fact is, the journey never ends. Y'shua grew in wisdom and stature[58] his whole life and if he can grow, certainly Adam and the rest of us can as well. In fact, the garden, just like the wilderness for Y'shua, was a testing place. Adam was given a job to do, he was to work and serve the garden. Service to the created order, the work of bringing about balance and harmony, is the function for which we were created. He was also given boundaries and rules. After all, if the trees were not put there as a test, why put them there at all, why would God place the seeds of failure within easy reach? Why take the risk of irrevocably harming all of creation? If, however, it was just another test on the journey, then it makes much more sense. Adam becomes more like Job, the *nechash* in this case taking on the role of the adversary. Due to his failure, Adam must take a step back, return to the previous place and begin to learn again. In this case, instead of serving the garden, he needed to learn how to serve the people. Y'shua taught that the greatest among his followers would be the one who served all[59]. It was true for him, it was true for Adam and it is true for us.

The question naturally arises, if life is a continuous journey and the garden of Eden was merely another testing place, what is beyond the garden? Obviously, our story does not take us there. In physics, there are those who speculate, and some theories that require multiple dimensions or universes beyond our own. Eden may be just one of many steps along the way to the goal. There are hints in the Scriptures and in other religious traditions of what it may mean to go beyond Eden. Adam, for instance, is never credited with the "miraculous." If

---

[58] Luke 2:40
[59] Mark 9:35

the ability to manipulate the probabilities of the underlying quantum mechanics is an ability manifested by those who went beyond Eden, then men like Moshe, Elijah and Y'shua have passed that test and moved on. Obviously, they have the ability to either move freely among these dimensions or to exist in several simultaneously. The scriptures also points out however, that there are certain places one goes, specifically when one dies, that unless one has achieved Y'shua's level of spiritual attainment, one does not come back from. Where is that place? The Scriptures call it *She'ol* which is merely the 'unknown place.' We may speculate as to what it is like, but there are few hints in the Scriptures and it was of little concern to Hebrew mindset of Moshe and the prophets. They were more interested in the here and now; flights of fantasy into the unknown would wait for the Greek mindset.

The point here is that life is a continual journey and that while Eden may be an immediate goal, it is not the ultimate one. Our role is the same as Adam's. We are to use the unique abilities we were created with to restore the harmony and balance within the created order. It is a life of service, a life that has no place for the ego. As we serve, as we remove the layers of delusion from our lives, we will begin to see the world as it really is. We will have our "eyes opened" to things our mind has kept us from seeing. We will move forward on the journey, passing tests or being sent back for reeducation, but always moving. The path of true enlightenment is the life of a nomad. What is the goal of a nomad? To become one with his environment for his sustenance and protection. What is our goal? To become one with the totality of creation, to experience things, all things, as they truly are, to merge with the rhythm of the universe as it dances under the direction of *Ayn Soph*.

Genesis 3:24

וַיְגָרֶשׁ אֶת־הָאָדָם וַיַּשְׁכֵּן מִקֶּדֶם לְגַן־עֵדֶן אֶת־הַכְּרֻבִים
וְאֵת לַהַט הַחֶרֶב הַמִּתְהַפֶּכֶת לִשְׁמֹר אֶת־דֶּרֶךְ עֵץ
הַחַיִּים: ס

**And he cast out the adam. And he caused the keruvim and the
lahat of the revolving sword, to dwell from the ancient times
for the protected region in Eden, to guard the road of the trees
of life.**

The deed is finally done, Adam is cast out of the garden for he and his
woman's indiscretion.

YHVH places two things to guard the road into the garden, the *keruvim*
and the *lahat*. The *lahat* is another entity guarding the way to the
garden whose name means "flame." This *lahat* is 'of' the 'revolving
sword.' The fact that the *keruvim* and the *lahat* are there to guard the
garden tells us something about it. First of all they are guarding in the
sense that they are restricting access, not preventing it altogether.
They are the "gatekeepers," so to speak. The Scriptures are full of the
imagery associated with these two things. We can start with the *lahat*.
The *lahat* is a reference to fire and because it is one of the
gatekeepers, one must go through the fire to get to the other side, in
this case, into the garden. The Scriptures refer to the "refining fire"
many times[60]. Metal is put into the refiner's fire to remove impurities.
We must go through a similar process to enter the garden. We have
surrounded ourselves with the husk of the ego and all the baggage we
add on to our lives has to be burned away. But we are more complex

---

[60] Malachi 3 being a prime example.

than that. In Y'shua's parable of the wheat and the tares, they grow together just as ore is mixed with impurities; the valuable metal is mixed in with the worthless. Just as the wheat and tares are separated at the harvest, the impurities are separated from the ore by the refiner's fire. Much of what is dross within ourselves is well hidden in the crevices and deep recesses of our being and it is only through the long and intense refining process that it is revealed and removed. Only when we have submitted to the work of the *lahat* will we enter the garden.

There is more, however. The *lahat* is joined by the *keruvim* who share the responsibility of controlling admittance to Eden. The word *Keruvim* (usually transliterated as cherubim) usually conjures an image of men in white robes adorned with wings and surrounded with light, but this imagery is of fairly recent origins. In the ancient world the *keruvim* were winged lions. As words and names traveled from one regional language to another, sounds shifted and KeRuV (the singular form of keruvim) becomes GRyF, a winged lion, in the Greek language, which is the origin of the English word 'griffin.' In the ancient Mesopotamian world, the *keruvim* were the guardians of the throne. The *keruvim* are prominently displayed on the mercy seat of the Ark of the Covenant, the Ark being the place where God came to meet with the people of Israel and could very well be referred to as the throne of God on the earth. The function of the Ark was to permit two way communications between YHVH and the people of Israel; it was a bridge between the Garden and the Earth, one dimension and the other. If the heavens are the throne of God and the earth is his footstool, the Ark was the portal from one world to the other and just like Eden; the way was guarded by the *keruvim*.

But the Ark is not the only way, as we have seen. The Burning Bush of Moshe performed the same function, although it emphasized the *lahat*. It was a thorn bush, paralleling the sword, and it was on fire. Elijah experienced the fiery chariot and the chariot, like the sword, is an implement of war. One of the key things emphasized in our translation is that the *keruvim* and the *lahat* have been there from 'ancient days,' just as Eden had[61]. The fact is that as long as the garden has been around, access to it has come through the *keruvim* and the *lahat*. In one form or another, if we want to follow in the footsteps of Adam, Moshe, Enoch, Elijah and Y'shua, we must endure the *lahat* and accommodate the *keruvim*.

Besides the *keruvim* and the *lahat* being found together on the road to the garden, there are additional similarities between the two. In this verse we read that the *lahat* is associated with a sword and in Jeremiah 2:3 we find the 'sword' being like a 'destroying lion.' In addition, the Hebrew word for 'sword' is *cherev*, a related cognate of the word *keruv*, a winged lion. Whatever the *keruvim* and *lahat* are, we know for certain they are very powerful guards and only one who is truly worthy will be allowed to pass through into the garden.

---

[61] See the Quantum Translation of Genesis 2:8.

Appendix - The Nomadic Lifestyle: the key to success as a person of God

Before specifically defining the nomadic lifestyle and what makes one part of it, a few words of introduction are in order. The core idea of this presentation is that the adaptation of a specific lifestyle will bring about a desired spiritual result. To some that may not seem an earth shattering revelation. It is, however, in opposition to the current western understanding of spirituality and religion. If one is a Christian, one needs to *believe* certain things and once one accepts certain 'facts,' one will become spiritual and the hope is that a lifestyle change will result. In Judaism, one converts to a community, again after acknowledging certain 'truths' and this 'spiritual' step will result in the desire to adapt a certain lifestyle. The key to both is a 'conversion' which is supposed to create spirituality. Spirituality is the result of becoming *mentally convinced* a certain set of beliefs are true. Lifestyle is a secondary result of the primary aim of conversion.

The proposal here is that a certain lifestyle, regardless of belief, creates spirituality and with it proper belief/worldview. We are defining spirituality this way-the expression of certain desirable characteristics such as love, the desire to help one's fellow man, a passion for justice as well as the more "spiritual" things such as 'experiencing God,' however that may be defined. Lifestyle creates proper belief and practice by necessity; belief or practices do not create lifestyle. We have all seen too many failures here. A new approach is necessary.

One of the basic questions we may ask is "How do I get in touch with God, how can I have an authentic spiritual experience." This is not the

227

place to define 'spiritual experience' but we can look at the examples in the biblical text for several clues. The clues will lead us to the conclusion that it is very rare for someone to have an encounter with God out of the blue even though it may occasionally appear that way. The patriarchs are the first and most obvious example. Avraham was a city dweller and he left Ur to sojourn in a land he was unfamiliar with. While travelling in the land of Canaan he encountered God on a regular basis. Yitzach and Ya'akov continued to live as nomads, never settling anywhere for long. When Israel settled in Egypt, they didn't hear from God until Moshe showed up. Moshe himself did not have his encounter with God until he left Egypt and spent forty years as a nomad (shepherd). Israel had internalized the values of Egypt to such a great extent that they rejected the promise of God as they stood on the threshold of taking the land. Only after the next generation grew up as nomads in the desert were they able to go into the land. David, the king 'after God's heart' developed that heart as a shepherd which is a basically nomadic lifestyle. Amos the prophet was a shepherd and many of them, like Elijah and Elisha were itinerant. Y'shua himself lived an itinerant lifestyle-'the son of man has no place to lay his head.' He required the same of his disciples.

The Bible is also filled with nomadic and agricultural imagery-shepherds, farmers, fields, millstones, etc. We don't believe it is an accident of history that God is most clearly revealed in this context. In fact, one cannot understand the Bible if one does not understand the values and culture of the nomad. We believe there are several identifiable traits of the nomadic lifestyle that draw people close to God and create desirable character traits. We also believe that the opposite is true. If we develop and become part of a culture that does not have nomadic characteristics or is, in fact, in opposition to it, one will find it difficult, if not impossible, to become an authentic spiritual person. The following are several characteristics of the nomadic lifestyle. Avraham will be our 'test case' although much of what is said will apply to other biblical characters.

#1 - Nomads are removed from the dominant cultures of their time

In Avraham's time the land of Canaan was relatively free of foreign entanglement. After Hammurabi and his descendants made Babylon great, it fell into decline at about 1600 BCE, ceasing to exert a broad influence. Egypt was invaded by the Hyscos around 1800 BCE and internal problems kept it busy for several centuries. This left the land of Canaan relatively free from their interference, political or otherwise. Its basic political entity was the city state whose influence was limited, and their power even more so. Ya'akov's sons could destroy the whole city of Shechem, including its king. Abimelech approached Yitzach and said the latter was too powerful for his city to handle. Avraham's household destroyed an army of four kings and rescued Lot. The point here is that the patriarchs were not forced to submit politically or culturally to anyone.

After the decline of Babylon/Persia and Egypt, Greece, and later Rome, became the cultural and political powerhouses. Today there are three dominant cultural and political influences. The first is western, and specifically, American. European culture as a whole has been in decline since the passing of the British Empire, but American culture and political influence is felt in most places in the world. The second is Islamic. Once it was the dominance of Arab armies that exercised their power, now it is oil. Islam is a fast growing religion and states that subscribe to it are not confined to the Middle East. Finally, there is far eastern culture, defined by India and China. Their influence is primarily through sheer numbers but they are in decline. Western influence is becoming more and more pervasive. China's adoption of Marxism, a western philosophy, accelerated that region's rejection of indigenous culture and Japan's loss in World War Two did the same for them.

Living a nomadic lifestyle or even adopting a nomadic character within political units that have adopted one of these three cultures is very difficult. Its feasibility will depend on several factors including geography, political system and the strength of the dominant culture and how seriously the people who are part of it take it. This is because cultural norms demand varying degrees of conformity to their customs and values. In a western democracy, one can choose not to participate in the civil religion without serious consequence. For example, one can choose not to celebrate Christmas or participate it in any way without going to jail or worse. In Islamic cultures, cultural conformity often has the force of law and the consequences for non-conformity are severe. That does not mean, however, it is easier to defy one or the other. One may conform out of a sense of fear or one can be, to put it bluntly, brainwashed. The totality of the legal, governmental, educational and entertainment systems are put in place to support the dominant culture. It is difficult and inconvenient not to participate in it. This is to say nothing of the force of law and regulation that support it. Western democracies, including American representative democracy, are socialist. By definition, this means that the power of regulation and taxation are used to reward certain behaviors and punish others, or even make them impossible. These behaviors are, obviously, those that support the dominant culture and those that don't.

Avraham, as we have seen, left the political and cultural entity that exerted such power over him. Among the city states of Canaan, he had nothing to fear legally or politically from the Canaanite kings around him because, quite simply, he was more powerful than they were. They could force Avraham to do nothing. Perhaps none of us can become militarily as powerful as Avraham but the truth is, the smaller the political entity, the less of a threat it is. As part of one of these dominant cultural/political entities, we are all at their mercy, mentally and physically. Avraham recognized these constraints. If a spiritual giant like Avraham saw bucking the dominant system as impossible, how can we claim otherwise?

#2 - Nomads needed to be self reliant

Our previous point showed that nomads were under no one's control, politically or culturally. The flip side is that they were under no one's protection either. The purpose of the state, be it a large country or a small Canaanite city-state, is for mutual protection and benefit. In order to receive the benefits of the state, one needs to give up some things. These include one's wealth (taxes-the state costs money), individuality (one is now identified with the state one is part of) and freedom (the state has the right to tell you what rules to follow to receive the benefits).

In the Bible the extreme illustration is the story of Yosef and the famine in Egypt. For protection from starvation, the state took all their money, their land and their freedom. The Egyptians became slaves for food. It is nearly always the case that people are willing to give up more freedom in a crisis. In the United States this has been illustrated time and time again. The depression gave us the 'New Deal' which has resulted in the largest governmental structure the world has ever seen. More recently, 'homeland security' and the surrounding issues raised by terrorism have brought up the issue of trading freedom for security. In cities, when there is a shooting, honest people are willing to give up their own freedom to protect themselves (gun ownership) in the hopes that it will curtail those who care not at all about other people's freedom or person. War, or the threat of physical harm, and poverty are the largest motivators for giving up freedom and personal responsibility and relying on the state to provide these necessities.

Once it begins, this slide from freedom takes on a life of its own. Western socialist democracies are the result of this. Personal responsibility is nullified because there is always someone else to blame for our troubles and there is the expectation that someone else

233

(the state) will take care of us and provide for our needs. In the United States, the pervasiveness of lawyers assists us with the first one- finding someone to blame (often for our own stupidity or risky behavior) and making them pay. In Europe where 'cradle to grave' welfare is the norm, there is always a program or handout to meet the needs of those who are too lazy or stupid to make it on their own. Forgive us if we sound a bit Darwinian but hunger and survival are great motivators. In many European nations, unemployment is more attractive than working. It pays more than the take home pay for many jobs because of the high taxation necessary to support universal welfare. And they wonder why unemployment remains high?! In the United States before the depression and the 'New Deal,' people were responsible for themselves, their own success and failure. Family ties were crucial because family and friends were the only 'safety net.' People worked harder because the price of failure was so great. Now we have turned the state into our parents, educators, family and community. We are more isolated because the primary relationship for all our necessities is between the individual and the state. The state, for its part, gladly fills this role because the tendency of all government is to exert more control over the governed. The more dependency government creates, the more control it can exert. Socialism is the opposite of nomadic self-reliance.

What is the result? We have insulated ourselves from the created order and spend our whole lives in an artificial environment doing things that have nothing to do with providing our basic necessities. If we are honest with ourselves, we realize we can't do anything for ourselves anymore. We do not have the ability to fend for ourselves. We go through over a decade of public education, we can read and write and add but if we were suddenly deprived of the comforts of western society, (like the grocery store or our pre-fab home) we would die of starvation and exposure very quickly. Prepared and frozen meals have made the basics of cooking obsolete for many. Many don't know the first thing about the fundamentals of construction. If our transportation gives out, we rarely know the first thing about how to fix it. Few engage in gardening, hunting or fishing. If our clothes rip we go out and buy new ones. We used to engage in hobbies that taught us these skills even though we no longer needed them to meet our basic needs. Now we spend so much time working so as to add more elements to our artificial world that we have little time for such pursuits.

The nomad had to be what we refer to as a 'jack of all trades.' Three thousand years after Avraham, he might have been called a 'renaissance man,' someone who does a lot of things well and knows a lot about a variety of subjects. When something went wrong in the middle of the wilderness, the nomad had to know how to deal with it. He was an expert in animal husbandry, he was an agriculturist, a carpenter, cook, tailor, warrior and a thousand other things. Y'shua taught that we should not worry about providing for ourselves and we should look at the lilies and the sparrows as examples. Most interpret this to mean that we do not worry because God Himself comes down from heaven and meets our needs on an individual basis just as he does the plants and animals. Just the opposite is true. When one is confident, prepared, skillfull and self assured, worry has no place. The lilies and sparrows know exactly how to provide their own needs. The sparrow does not fly around stressed out as to where to find food or how to build a nest. They *know* how to do it. If we knew how to provide our basic needs, we would not be stressed either. We may be inconvenienced on occasion, but when one's life is simple and one knows how to provide one's basic needs, what is there to be worried about?

The nomad was also responsible for his own safety. He did not have the state to protect him, and although we may think otherwise, neither do we. Sure, the state may be able to protect us from invasion by say, Canada, but who is going to protect you from the mugger or rapist or gang or terrorist? We do not have policemen on every corner nor should we. So it comes down to us, can we protect our person and property? I would say that the vast majority of us cannot. And many of us have been taught that we shouldn't. Christianity and Judaism are now known as pacifist religions. Violence is discouraged and training to be violent, even in self defense, is not generally an acceptable practice. We have been taught that the truly spiritual person has God to protect him. No, the truly spiritual person is aware of his surroundings and any danger therein and has the ability and confidence to deal with it. Today, a nomad knows how to fight and shoot a gun. His family or clan can be quickly organized for self defense. I would dare say that few of us have this ability yet today's world demands it even if we are not nomadic. Think about this, if we reversed the roles of the hijackers and the hijacked on 9/11, would the result have been the same? Do you think a couple of civilian Americans would have been able to take over a plane of Arabs with just boxcutters?! I don't think so, the Arabs would have fought back because their culture is different. We have been taught that our defense in not under our control. But it is our person, our life, and it should not be so easily turned over to the state, especially with the knowledge that practically, the state cannot fulfill its obligation. We should all have the skills necessary for our protection and provision. Self reliance is one of the keys to the nomadic life.

#3 - Nomads were always immigrants and outsiders

By definition, a nomad has no national ties nor is he tied to anyone beyond his small family group. A nomad was never part of the 'in' group. A nomad is different in dress, speech, custom and worship than those of the surrounding peoples they encounter. In the days of Avraham the nomad was distrusted by the indigenous peoples and the nomad distrusted them. They were constantly wary of one another because they were different. Too often in our day, this translates into a 'one man against the world' mentality, particularly among religious folks. They alone have the truth, they alone live the right way, they alone are close to God and everyone else is lost, confused and/or going to hell. This makes such people offensive to those around them for they think only of themselves and their supposed 'holiness' or 'purity.' Such people rarely bring anyone closer to God. Y'shua rightly described them thus; "you go over land and sea to make one convert and make him twice the son of hell you are!" Difference, even if it leads to success, is no reason for feelings of superiority.

The reason for this is that while there may have been distrust among nomads and indigenous people, they needed each other and developed symbiotic relationships. The nomad needed the acceptance of the surrounding peoples to survive and prosper. They needed to be diplomatic and cordial. The hellfire and brimstone religious crowd could learn a lesson here. As the saying goes, 'you attract a lot more bees with honey than with vinegar.' As Hebrews 12:14 states, "Strive for peace with all men, and for the holiness without which no one will see the Lord". There is parallelism at work here. Everyone wants to know how to be holy. The answer is that one is supposed to be in *shalom* with man and the world. But, you say, holiness means

237

'separation' and that is true. A person who is in harmony with all will stand out as unique from the rest of humanity.

We must be careful however. We can never sacrifice our integrity or values for the sake of *shalom*, for *shalom* will not be the result if we do. Some religious folks have attempted to be too accommodating. For example, some churches have Halloween parties, Chanukah often becomes Christmas. The nomad, while cordial, must maintain his separation. Lot is a prime example. He moved close to Sodom and then into Sodom. He ceased being a nomad and would have been caught up in the destruction of the city had it not been for Avraham's intervention. Ya'akov could have become part of the Shechemites as well and disappeared as a separate group if Simeon and Levi had not killed all the inhabitants. For a nomad, it was a fine line that needed to be walked. They needed to respect the customs of the surrounding peoples while maintaining their own unique identity and they remained free of personal entanglements that would endanger their way of life.

Today, the line is just as difficult. I have already given some examples but the most important and pervasive problems are those we deal with every day. 1 Peter 2:11 says, "Beloved, I beseech you as aliens and exiles to abstain from the passions of the flesh that wage war against your soul."

The flesh could be defined as the ego. The truth is, whether you are one who goes toward the accommodating course of action or the 'stand alone against the world' path, the desire to satisfy the ego is at the root. The accommodator wants to be liked. We constantly do things that are influenced by what other people think of us. We want people to like us, we want to create a favorable impression, we want to fit in. Our culture defines what that means. Too often this leads to entanglements and unnecessary compromise. The stand alone person is simply an attention getter. He gets his ego stroked by getting noticed. In religious circles, this is the overly and outwardly pious person. In the secular culture it may be the pierced and tattooed crowd. The key is the ego. The nomad didn't care about such things. He did what he did out of necessity, his viewpoint was basically utilitarian. The key difference was that he understood the value of people and the world around him. He would not use people as objects, but treated all with respect and dignity. Even Ya'akov blessed Pharaoh when he was going to sojourn in his land. Some of this may seem contradictory but it takes a lot of wisdom to walk the narrow line the nomad did.

#4 - Nomads were pastoral, not urban.

This is related to number two, the need for self reliance. In a city or town, everyone relies on everyone else. We fill our little niche, our job or craft, and know little else. Someone else fixes things that break, someone else grows our food, someone else builds our shelter, provides our utilities and countless other things. The interesting thing is that even though our time is no longer taken up with our basic provision, life in a city or town (any socially organized permanent society) is very busy. There is always somewhere to go, something to do, some set of requirements or expectations such a society puts on the individuals within it that need to be met. We have to go somewhere to buy our necessities as we do not produce them at home. We need to go to work somewhere away from home. Society expects some involvement, so there are events to go to or things our children are expected to be a part of. If there are no such needs, society creates them through entertainment and advertising. All these things vie for our attention and take up our time. We wait in line, we wait in traffic, we wait through commercials.

Because we spend so much time waiting (doing nothing), the somethings we do must be made quicker, easier and more convenient. We fill our lives with time and labor saving devices. Take mealtime, for example. Not only do we not grow our own food, few take the time to prepare it. We don't have time to spend an hour or two to take raw food and turn it into something nutritious and natural. We would rather pop something into the microwave so we can have more time for other busy things. In the nomadic camp the preparation of meals gave time for mothers and daughters and the other women of the camp to socialize or just spend time in reflection. Mealtime itself was attended to by the whole family and was the social event of the day. How often do most families do that anymore?

240

Cities are noisy. There are always a million things going on and they all want our attention. With all the noise how can we expect to hear from God? If we try to sit still we can't because our culture has branded stillness as idleness and laziness. So if we try to do it we find we are bored. We have been conditioned to believe we must constantly be stimulated or entertained. We fill this need through work or popular entertainment. We have lost our imagination. Children who once had crafts and projects, tree houses and go-carts now watch T.V. or play video games. Adults are no better, their toys for passivity are merely more expensive. "Be still and know that I am God." Can we be still long enough to know anything?

As nomadic people went about their work, they talked; they spent time getting to know one another. I mentioned that women talked during mealtime. Men talked during work and work events such as at harvest or shearing time and these were true social events. Everyone wants to know how to get to know God. If you and I are created in his image, getting to know one another is a good start. This is the opposite of the Christian ideal of the monk who lives alone in contemplation or the Jewish sage who is buried in books. This takes time and effort to get to know people and we don't often make it or have it. If we have one good friend we consider ourselves fortunate. Usually we are content to live our lives vicariously through the people we see on T.V. What we need to do is get out there and live, do something, go somewhere, meet someone. Nomads were not loners, they had a vibrant social structure. The isolation fostered on us by our busy city lives serves only to keep us trapped, alone and spiritually dead.

The reality is, we know we need to spend 'quiet time' with God. Some religious groups organize retreats to force people to do this although often they are so scheduled and structured time is not to be found.

But the idea of the retreat, to leave the city for the woods, the idea that getting back to nature gets us closer to God is a truth that springs from deep within us. The nomad lived close to nature all the time. He knew its moods, its patterns, and by understanding it and becoming part of it he knew a lot about God. Paul said that the creation reveals the Creator[62]. Job tells us that the creation teaches us[63]. In the artificial environment of the city we cannot experience this. Through constant exposure to and dependence on the creation, we are forced to become one with the totality of God and His order. We may wish for it in an urban setting but it is only gained through physical experience.

---

[62] Romans 1:20
[63] Job 12:7-10; 35:11

#5 - Nomads demonstrated strong decisive leadership

In a pastoral society, the father or patriarch of the family was the absolute authority. He was the master of his household. He decided when to leave and when to set up camp, he conducted all business, he arranged marriages and was the sole source of justice in legal matters. At times, he delegated this authority to his sons, or more rarely to others, but there was no question where the buck stopped. It was Ya'akov who decided when to go back to Egypt during the famine, Yehudah ordered Tamar to be burnt for harlotry, Avraham sent his servant to find a wife for his son.

The reason such strong authority was necessary was because there was no safety net in nomadic society. The decisions made could lead either to the prosperity or the death of the whole clan. The line between life and death for a nomad was easy to cross and it could happen very quickly. The father needed to be knowledgeable, decisive, experienced and wise. He raised his children, particularly his sons, to take his place, learn from his mistakes and carry on the traditions, not because they were nice ideas but because the future of the clan depended on it. If he didn't pass on what he learned to his children, the clan would die.

Current western culture frowns on such activity. It goes all the way back to the Middle Ages at least. The vast majority of the populations were serfs, tied to the land with no opportunity to rise up or make decisions. The church discouraged reading so people would not think for themselves. The nobles and the clergy set themselves up as 'experts' inferring that the general populace could not make wise decisions. Today we are in a similar situation. 'Experts' and 'specialists' abound and their word is respected and believed, no matter how outrageous it may seem. This is especially true where government is concerned. When someone is elected to high office, suddenly they become experts in everything from finances to medicine to military affairs to law to technology to ethics. If we question such things without position or several letters behind our names we are just kooks and uneducated fools. If we want to make a big decision or take decisive action, we are questioned mercilessly. It is a result of the feminization of our society. If men are decisive and strong they are Neanderthals. Women who are decisive are 'butches.' No one is supposed to be self-assured and resolute.

The key here is that we have been taught to think of other people before ourselves. Now, this is a piece of accepted wisdom that has been popularized and supported by the Bible. We suffer men like Hitler because we would rather see people suffer under a dictator than destroy the illusion of peace. We afford more rights to criminals than victims. We suffer injustice because we don't want to offend or hurt someone's feelings. Nomads didn't consider such things and when we project our western values on them we end up with what in our minds are contradictions. For example, we wonder how God could instruct the Israelites to exterminate the people of Canaan. It is not the right question. "What will insure the survival and prosperity of the clan?" That is the right question. They did not eliminate the Canaanites and they suffered as a result. When Lot was taken by the four kings in their attack on Sodom, Avraham didn't ask whether the kings needed the goods or whether they were right in crushing the rebellion or whether it was a legal and just war. He needed to rescue a member of his clan and he did what was necessary, resulting in the death of a lot of people. Simeon and Levi understood that accepting the immoral actions of Shechem would result in the moral disintegration of the clan and they exacted justice for the actions and intents of the people of the city. We do not need to put up with injustice or have our prosperity denied for the sake of false peace or out of fear. The nomads did not, for they did not let fear rule their lives. Their mantra was "peace through strength," not "peace through appeasement."

#6 - Among Nomads, the overriding legal responsibility was hospitality.

Not only do we see the crucial nature of hospitality in the stories of the patriarchs but it is codified in the Torah as well. The need for keeping found articles safe until the owner returns and providing safe haven for slaves are just two examples. The teachings of Y'shua support this as well, particularly the parable of the 'good Samaritan.' The answer to the question of 'who is my neighbor/brother' is whoever understands and acts on the obligations of hospitality. A few practical examples of this are Avraham's service to his three 'guests,' Lot's protection of the messengers to Sodom, and Rachel's provision for Avraham's servant. Hospitality was not just being nice. It may, at times, be a necessity for survival in the harsh wilderness. All nomads shared the same risks and helped each other out in this way; a 'do unto others as you would have them do unto you' code that they lived by.

Hospitality, however, was not free. It was an intricate social and legal obligation that was understood by each side. Therefore, it was not something that was offered or accepted lightly. The host obligated himself to provide for and protect his guests. That we all understand. The one receiving the hospitality also had an obligation to bless the household with whatever he had. Avraham's servant gave gifts of gold to Rachel. Lot's guests provided deliverance. Elisha provided a child to the couple that housed him. When the men came to Avraham, he offered his hospitality and they accepted. They then blessed him with Isaac. Not only that, but the contraction of hospitality put Avraham on an equal level with his guests which then allows him to argue with YHVH about Sodom.

246

There is one other crucial idea on which hospitality is based. The giving of hospitality is the demonstration of the belief that all people are afforded basic respect and dignity. Even an enemy was at peace when accepting the hospitality of a nomad. To a nomad, no one was an object, each person had value. The nomad understood that we all share the image of God and that living in harmony with all men and their surroundings was their objective. When the nomad achieved that balance, that harmony with the created order, that is, when he and we, can experience God as we were meant to.

In Conclusion

The nomadic lifestyle is the complete opposite of what most of us now live. I should say all because if you get e-mail or have a computer, chances are you are or are becoming westernized. We have been taught to value 'things,' and these 'things' are our wealth. To a nomad, having 'things,' was not important. When you had to carry around everything you owned, not much was retained. Avraham's wealth walked on its own. Solomon and his accumulation of wealth in the form of possessions led to Israel's downfall. This is one area where one can easily see how lifestyle leads to correct belief/worldview. If you cannot have a lot of possessions, you no longer think about accumulating them. Things become less important. In western culture, accumulation is everything, we are taught to be good consumers and we hope our children are even better consumers that we are. We have our homes filled with stuff, most of which is useless junk, some of which we pack in boxes when we move and stays packed until the next move. Yet we become so attached to our 'stuff' that they become our identity. The process of divesting ourselves of all our useless junk is difficult, but all that 'stuff' merely takes up time and space in our lives that could be better spent on other things.

This lifestyle change is key. Being self contained and mobile forces one to simplify and de-accumulate. Everything one owns becomes valuable not because of appearance but functionality. More importantly, one's sphere of concern shrinks down to a manageable size. Much of our stress, and by extension disease, results from so much of our lives being out of our control. So many of the things that affect us, directly and intimately, are things that concern ourselves with, but have no control over: from the chemicals that are put in our food to the taxes we pay for the car to the plumbing we can't fix to our child's education to our jobs and retirement to whether we wear a seat belt or not. Within the self contained nomadic lifestyle, there is little one can't fix, you are your own boss and one is not stuck within an oppressive socio-political environment, instead you can pick up and move. This is one of the reasons I like camping so much. When camping, the world is shrunk to the size of the campsite. No boss, no job, no house, nothing except what is in the campsite. It is developing a life in which the world is reduced to a manageable size.

Finally, being a nomad is different from being a traveler. There are people who retire, buy a huge motor home and travel the country. They are not nomads. They are just as attached to society as they were before they left; they are not allowing the lifestyle to change their attitudes. My personal opinion is that one of the few authentic nomad avenues open to us today is the cruising lifestyle. For the uninitiated, that means traveling the world on a sailboat. It allows freedom of movement, it removes any one government's authority and entanglement and once the initial expense is over, it can be a very cheap and rewarding life that is available to anyone, regardless of age.

We are living in an age when the Pax Americana is coming to an end and socialist western democracies are deteriorating under their own weight. Economic uncertainty, civil unrest and political deterioration may make the wealthy western lifestyle untenable in the future. To many, this will be a crushing blow. To those who think wealth is their right as westerners and Christians, this will be a true test of faith. To the nomad, it is an opportunity. For people who know how to provide for themselves and for whom wealth accumulation is a distant secondary concern, the economic travails that surround us are of little import. A nomad is free to follow prosperity without national consideration. Nomads are survivors and know how to maintain a fulfilling lifestyle regardless of external circumstances. It is the wisdom of experience and the ability to adapt that makes them so. It is a lifestyle that develops godly character and puts us in touch with that which is beyond us. In our times, it is a lifestyle we should all be considering seriously.

Genesis, Zen and Quantum Physics

CPSIA information can be obtained
at www.ICGtesting.com
Printed in the USA
BVHW070303281220
596442BV00005B/342